Introduction to Bookkeeping

Workbook

David Cox
Michael Fardon

Published by Osborne Books Limited
Tel 01905 748071
Email books@osbornebooks.co.uk
Website www.osbornebooks.co.uk

Design by Laura Ingham

Printed by CPI Group (UK) Limited, Croydon, CR0 4YY, on environmentally friendly, acid-free paper from managed forests.

British Library Cataloguing in Publication Data
A catalogue record for this book is available from the British Library

ISBN 978-1-911198-51-2

Contents

Introduction

Chapter activities

Answers to chapter activities

Practice assessments – tasks

Answers to practice assessments

Introduction

Qualifications covered

This book has been written specifically to cover the Unit 'Introduction to Bookkeeping' which is mandatory for the following qualifications:

AAT Level 2 Certificate in Accounting

AAT Level 2 Certificate in Bookkeeping

AAT Certificate in Accounting – SCQF Level 6

This book contains Chapter Activities which provide extra practice material in addition to the activities included in the Osborne Books Tutorial text, and Practice Assessments to prepare the student for the computer based assessments. The latter are based directly on the structure, style and content of the sample assessment material provided by the AAT at www.aat.org.uk.

Suggested answers to the Chapter Activities and Practice Assessments are set out in this book.

Osborne Study and Revision Materials

Additional materials, tailored to the needs of students studying this unit and revising for the assessment, include:

- **Tutorials:** paperback books with practice activities
- **Wise Guides:** pocket-sized spiral bound revision cards
- **Student Zone:** access to Osborne Books online resources
- **Osborne Books App:** Osborne Books ebooks for mobiles and tablets

Visit www.osbornebooks.co.uk for details of study and revision resources and access to online material.

Chapter
activities

1   The accounting system

1.1   A sale for immediate settlement made at a shop using a bank debit card is known as:

(a) A cash sale	
(b) A credit sale	
(c) A debit sale	

Which **one** of these options is correct?

1.2   An entry in a book of prime entry is:

(a) An entry in the ledger accounts of a business	
(b) An entry in the trial balance of a business	
(c) The first place an entry is recorded in the accounting records	

Which **one** of these options is correct?

1.3   The 'ledger' system of accounts is normally set up for recording:

(a) Cash transactions only	
(b) Cash and credit transactions only	
(c) Cash and credit and other financial transactions	

Which **one** of these options is correct?

1.4   A receivables ledger control account contains the totals of accounts of:

(a)	Customers who buy goods and services on a cash basis	
(b)	Customers who buy goods and services on a credit basis	
(c)	Suppliers who sell goods and services on a cash basis	
(d)	Suppliers who sell goods and services on a credit basis	

Which **one** of these options is correct?

1.5   Select the missing words from the selection below to complete the following text:

A [＿＿＿＿＿＿＿] sets out in two columns the balances of the

[＿＿＿＿＿＿＿] of a business.

The [＿＿＿＿＿＿＿] of the two columns should [＿＿＿＿＿＿＿]. The debit column

includes the accounts of [＿＿＿＿＿＿＿] and the credit column includes the accounts of

[＿＿＿＿＿＿＿]. This provides the [＿＿＿＿＿＿＿] of a business with important and

useful financial information.

Choose from:

payables	**agree**	**ledger accounts**	**managers**
receivables	**totals**	**trial balance**	

1.6   General ledger contains the accounts of:

(a) Trade payables	
(b) Trade receivables	
(c) Assets, liabilities, income and expenses	
(d) Suppliers and customers	

Which **one** of these options is correct?

1.7   The statement of profit or loss shows:

(a) Assets – Income = Profit	
(b) Income – Expenses = Profit	
(c) Expenses – Liabilities = Profit	

Which **one** of these options is correct?

1.8   The statement of financial position shows:

(a) Assets + Income = Capital	
(b) Assets – Liabilities = Capital	
(c) Assets + Capital = Liabilities	

Which **one** of these options is correct?

2   Financial documents for sales

2.1   Praxis Stationery has supplied the following goods to a credit customer, Dover Designs.

The list price of the goods is £4.00 per box file, plus VAT at 20%. Dover Designs is to be given a 20% trade discount and a 2% prompt payment discount for settlement within 14 days.

DELIVERY NOTE	No 246
PRAXIS STATIONERY	**Date** 09 07 20-3
45 Jarvis Street	
Mereford MR1 2GH	
Dover Designs	
68 Whitecliff Street, Granstow, GR3 7GH	Customer code DO109

100 Box files, Code BX100

(a)   **You are to** complete the following invoice:

INVOICE

PRAXIS STATIONERY
45 Jarvis Street
Mereford MR1 2GH
VAT Reg 831 8627 06

To
Dover Designs
68 Whitecliff Street, Granstow, GR3 7GH

No 1689

Date 09 07 20-3

Customer code

Delivery note no

Quantity	Product code	Unit price (£)	Total (£)	Net (£)	VAT (£)	Total (£)

(b)   If Dover Designs decides to take advantage of the prompt payment discount, it will take which **one** of the following actions:

(a)	Reduce the amount of the invoice total by 2%	
(b)	Request Praxis Stationery to issue a new invoice	
(c)	Request a credit note for the amount of the discount (including VAT)	

Which **one** of these options is correct?

2.2   The following transactions have been passed through the account of Rosetti Associates, a new credit customer of Praxis Limited:

Date	Document	Amount £
1 August	Invoice 1748	4,567.89
9 August	Invoice 1778	2,457.60
10 August	Invoice 1783	4,678.30
17 August	Credit note 319	280.50
29 August	Cheque	4,287.39

You are to complete the statement of account shown below:

STATEMENT OF ACCOUNT
PRAXIS STATIONERY
45 Jarvis Street, Mereford MR1 2GH

To Rosetti Associates
Date 31 08 20-3

Date	Details	Amount £	Balance outstanding £
1 August	Invoice 1748		
9 August	Invoice 1778		
10 August	Invoice 1783		
17 August	Credit note 319		
29 August	Cheque		

2.3 Praxis Limited codes all sales invoices with a customer code and a general ledger code.

A selection of the codes used is given below.

Customer	Customer Account Code
Artex Ltd	ART09
Bristol Wholesale	BRI25
Britmore Ltd	BRI45
Coleman Trading	COL10
Coldring Limited	COL12

Item	General Ledger Code
Paper products	GL4002
Pens	GL4003
Storage	GL4008
Printer inks	GL4017
Files	GL4018

Indicate in the table below the appropriate customer and general ledger codes that would be applied to the following sales invoices:

Product	Customer	General Ledger Code	Customer Code
Copy paper	Britmore Ltd		
Gel pens	Coldring Limited		
Box files	Artex Limited		
Black printer ink	Coleman Trading		
Archive storage boxes	Bristol Wholesale		
Suspension files	Britmore Limited		

2.4 The financial document which is sent by the seller of goods or services and reduces the amount due to the seller is:

(a) A refund note	
(b) A debit note	
(c) A credit note	

Which **one** of these options is correct?

2.5 A business sells goods which have a list price of £800. The following discounts are available to the buyer:

- 20% trade discount

- 5% prompt payment discount for settlement within 14 days

(a) The sales invoice should show a VAT amount (at 20%) of:

(a) £121.60	
(b) £128.00	
(c) £160.00	

Which **one** of these options is correct?

(b) The total price for the goods on the invoice should be:

(a) £729.60	
(b) £768.00	
(c) £960.00	

Which **one** of these options is correct?

2.6   This task is about calculating prompt payment discount.

You are the bookkeeper at Cookley Limited. Today, 10 April 20-7, you have issued the two invoices below to customers.

Cookley Ltd	
Invoice no: 4551	
To: Wyre plc	
Date: 10 April 20-7	

	£
50 x Product 68 at £10 each	500.00
VAT @ 20%	100.00
TOTAL	600.00

Terms: 3% discount if payment received within 10 days of date of invoice

Cookley Ltd	
Invoice no: 4552	
To: CDS Ltd	
Date: 10 April 20-7	

	£
80 x Product 95 at £12 each	960.00
VAT @ 20%	192.00
TOTAL	1,152.00

Terms: 2.5% discount if payment received within 14 days of date of invoice

(a)   The accounts supervisor asks you to:

- calculate how much will be received from each customer if the prompt payment discount is taken

- calculate the date by which the amounts will be received if the prompt payment discount is taken   (choose from the date options below)

Customer	£	Date
Wyre plc		
CDS Ltd		

Date options
10 April 20-7
20 April 20-7
21 April 20-7
24 April 20-7
25 April 20-7

(b)   In which ledger of Cookley Ltd's bookkeeping system will the accounts of Wyre plc and CDS Ltd be kept?

(a) Payables ledger	
(b) General ledger	
(c) Receivables ledger	

Which **one** of these options is correct?

3 Double-entry and the accounting equation

3.1 Where does double-entry take place?

(a)	In the trial balance	
(b)	In the books of prime entry	
(c)	In the ledgers	
(d)	In the day books	

Which **one** of these options is correct?

3.2 The ledger that contains the accounts of suppliers is the:

(a)	Payables ledger	
(b)	General ledger	
(c)	Receivables ledger	

Which **one** of these options is correct?

3.3   The table below lists payments and receipts of a business which pass through the Bank Account. Write the names of the two accounts involved in the double-entry in the correct columns. The first entry is completed to show what is required. The name of the account which is not the Bank account is shown in bold type in the left-hand column.

	Debit	Credit
Money paid for **Purchases**	Purchases	Bank
Money received from **Sales**		
Rent paid for premises used		
Rent received for premises let		
Motor expenses paid		
Payment for **advertising** costs		
Stationery bill paid		
Loan received		
Loan repayment made		

3.4   The Bank Account shown below has been written up by the bookkeeper, but the double-entry has not yet been done. Use the blank accounts set out on the next page by completing the account name, date details and amount for each entry.

Dr			Bank Account			Cr
2013		£	2013			£
1 Feb	Sales	5,000	1 Feb	Purchases		3,500
2 Feb	Sales	7,500	2 Feb	Wages		2,510
3 Feb	Bank Loan	12,500	3 Feb	Purchases		5,000
5 Feb	Sales	9,300	4 Feb	Rent paid		780

Debit			.... Account		Credit
Date	Details	£	Date	Details	£

Debit			.... Account		Credit
Date	Details	£	Date	Details	£

Debit			.... Account		Credit
Date	Details	£	Date	Details	£

Debit			.... Account		Credit
Date	Details	£	Date	Details	£

Debit			.... Account		Credit
Date	Details	£	Date	Details	£

3.5 Financial accounting is based upon the accounting equation.

(a) Show whether the following statements are true or false.

Statement		True	False
(a)	Liabilities equals capital plus assets		
(b)	Assets equals liabilities minus capital		
(c)	Capital equals assets minus liabilities		

(b) Classify each of the following items as an asset or a liability.

Item		Asset	Liability
(a)	Vehicles		
(b)	Bank loan		
(c)	Money owing by trade receivables		
(d)	Inventory		
(e)	Cash		
(f)	VAT owing to HM Revenue & Customs		

3.6 Fill in the missing figures:

Assets	Liabilities	Capital
£	£	£
50,000	0	....
40,000	10,000	....
55,200	....	30,250
....	18,220	40,760
40,320	15,980	....
....	24,760	48,590

3.7 An increase or a decrease in an asset or liability or capital will result in either a debit or a credit to the asset, liability or capital accounts.

Indicate with a tick whether a debit or credit will result from the transactions in the column on the left.

Transaction	Debit	Credit
(a) Capital account increases		
(b) Liability account increases		
(c) Asset account decreases		
(d) Liability account decreases		
(e) Asset account increases		

3.8 The table below sets out account balances from the books of a business. The opening capital is £20,000 which has been paid into the business bank account.

The columns (a) to (f) show the account balances resulting from a series of financial transactions that have taken place over time.

You are to compare each set of adjacent columns – ie (a) with (b), (b) with (c), and so on – and state, with figures, what financial transactions have taken place in each case. The first has been completed for you.

Ignore VAT.

	(a)	(b)	(c)	(d)	(e)	(f)
	£	£	£	£	£	£
Assets						
Vehicles	–	10,000	10,000	10,000	18,000	18,000
Inventory	–	–	6,000	9,000	9,000	9,000
Bank	20,000	10,000	4,000	4,000	1,000	11,000
Liabilities						
Loan	–	–	–	–	5,000	5,000
Payables	–	–	–	3,000	3,000	3,000
Capital	20,000	20,000	20,000	20,000	20,000	30,000

Answer (a) - (b): Vehicles have been bought for £10,000, paid from the bank

3.9 Enter the transactions listed below in the double-entry accounts. All the transactions pass through the Bank account so you will have to write the entries in the Bank account and work out what the other account entry will be. No credit sales or purchases are involved.

You can draw up your own accounts, photocopy the accounts on page 85 of the Tutorial, or download blank accounts from the Osborne Books website (www.osbornebooks.co.uk).

Date 20-4	Transaction
4 March	Paid in capital of £5,000
5 March	Received bank loan of £15,000
7 March	Sales of £670
11 March	Purchases of £375
15 March	Paid rent of £400
16 March	Purchases of £1,380
18 March	Sales of £430
22 March	Paid telephone bill £180
26 March	Sales of £1,320
29 March	Paid insurance of £1,200

3.10   The date is 31 August 20-4. You work as a bookkeeper for Beechwood Tools, a business that sells tools and equipment to the construction trade. You have been asked to balance the four accounts shown below.

(a)

Dr			Egret Building (Receivables Ledger)			Cr
20-4	**Details**	**£**	**20-4**	**Details**		**£**
24 Aug	Sales	900.00	25 Aug	Sales returns		160.00
27 Aug	Sales	140.00				
28 Aug	Sales	360.00				

(b)

Dr			Curtis & Curtis (Payables Ledger)			Cr
20-4	**Details**	**£**	**20-4**	**Details**		**£**
			24 Aug	Purchases		496.00
			26 Aug	Purchases		157.50
			31 Aug	Purchases		360.00

(c)

Dr	R & T Engineering (Payables Ledger)				Cr
20-4	**Details**	**£**	**20-4**	**Details**	**£**
24 Aug	Purchases returns	160.00	25 Aug	Purchases	240.00
			28 Aug	Purchases	720.00
			31 Aug	Purchases	340.00

(d)

Dr	Motor expenses (General Ledger)				Cr
20-4	**Details**	**£**	**20-4**	**Details**	**£**
5 Aug	Bank	150.40			
7 Aug	Bank	382.00			
9 Aug	Bank	69.30			
16 Aug	Bank	126.90			

4 Accounting for sales, returns and discounts

4.1 Which **one** of the following is a financial document?

(a)	Sales day book
(b)	Credit note
(c)	Receivables ledger account of P Lane
(d)	Sales account

4.2 Which **one** of the following is in the right order?

(a)	Sales returns account; VAT account; receivables ledger control account; customer's account; credit note issued; sales returns day book
(b)	Sales returns day book; receivables ledger control account; customer's account; sales returns account; VAT account; credit note issued
(c)	Sales returns day book; credit note issued; customer's account; sales returns account; VAT account; receivables ledger control account
(d)	Credit note issued; sales returns day book; sales returns account; VAT account; receivables ledger control account; customer's account

4.3 Which **one** of the following is entered in the sales day book?

(a)	Credit note
(b)	Purchase order
(c)	Statement of account sent to B Roberts, a trade receivable
(d)	Invoice

For Activities 4.4 and 4.5:

- work in pounds and pence, where appropriate

- the rate of Value Added Tax is to be calculated at 20% (when calculating VAT amounts, you should ignore fractions of a penny, ie round down to a whole penny)

- use a coding system incorporating the following:

sales day book	*– SDB65*	*general ledger account numbers*	
sales returns day book	*– SRDB22*	*receivables ledger control account*	*– GL1200*
		sales account	*– GL4100*
receivables ledger account numbers		*sales returns account*	*– GL4110*
Dines Stores	*– RL086*	*Value Added Tax account*	*– GL2200*
Meadow Golf Club	*– RL135*		
Raven Retailers Ltd	*– RL170*		
Teme Sports Ltd	*– RL178*		
Wyvern Stores	*– RL195*		

4.4   Pensax Products Limited manufactures and sells sports goods. During November 20-4 the following credit transactions took place:

20-4

3 Nov   Sold goods to Dines Stores £265 + VAT, invoice no 3592 issued

5 Nov   Sold goods to Raven Retailers Limited £335 + VAT, invoice no 3593 issued

6 Nov   Sold goods to Meadow Golf Club £175 + VAT, invoice no 3594 issued

10 Nov   Sold goods to Wyvern Stores £455 + VAT, invoice no 3595 issued

11 Nov   Sold goods to Dines Stores £290 + VAT, invoice no 3596 issued

13 Nov   Sold goods to Teme Sports Limited £315 + VAT, invoice no 3597 issued

17 Nov   Sold goods to Raven Retailers Limited £1,120 + VAT, invoice no 3598 issued

19 Nov   Sold goods to Teme Sports Limited £825 + VAT, invoice no 3599 issued

21 Nov   Sold goods to Dines Stores £354 + VAT, invoice no 3600 issued

24 Nov   Sold goods to Meadow Golf Club £248 + VAT, invoice no 3601 issued

27 Nov   Sold goods to Wyvern Stores £523 + VAT, invoice no 3602 issued

You are to:

(a)   Record the above transactions in Pensax Products' sales day book for November 20-4, using the format shown on the next page.

(b)   Record the accounting entries in Pensax Products' general ledger and receivables ledger. (You will need to retain the ledger accounts for use with Activity 4.5.)

Sales Day Book						SDB65
Date	Customer name	Invoice number	Account code	Total £	VAT £	Net £

4.5 The following details are the sales returns of Pensax Products Limited for November 20-4. They are to be:

(a) Recorded in the sales returns day book for November 20-4, using the format shown on the next page.

(b) Recorded in the general ledger and receivables ledger (use the ledgers already prepared in the answer to Activity 4.4).

20-4

10 Nov   Dines Stores returns goods £55 + VAT, credit note no 831 issued

14 Nov   Wyvern Stores returns goods £60 + VAT, credit note no 832 issued

19 Nov   Meadow Golf Club returns goods £46 + VAT, credit note no 833 issued

24 Nov   Teme Sports Limited returns goods £127 + VAT, credit note no 834 issued

28 Nov   Dines Stores returns goods £87 + VAT, credit note no 835 issued

Sales Returns Day Book						SRDB22
Date	Customer name	Credit note number	Account code	Total £	VAT £	Net £

4.6 Sales invoices have been prepared and partially recorded in the sales day book, as shown below.

(a) Complete the entries in the sales day book by inserting the appropriate figures for each invoice.

(b) Total the last five columns of the sales day book.

Sales day book

Date 20-4	Customer name	Invoice number	Total £	VAT £	Net £	Sales type 1 £	Sales type 2 £
30 June	Olander Ltd	1895		320		1,600	
30 June	Boltz & Co	1896	5,040				4,200
30 June	Ravells	1897	576		480	480	
	Totals						

4.7   You are employed by Beacon Limited as an Accounts Assistant. The business has a manual accounting system. Double-entry takes place in the general ledger; individual accounts of trade receivables are kept as subsidiary accounts in the receivables ledger. The VAT rate is 20%.

Notes:

- show your answer with a tick, words or figures, as appropriate

- coding is not required

(a)   The following credit transactions all took place on 30 June 20-7 and have been entered into the sales day book as shown below. No entries have yet been made in the ledgers.

Sales day book

Date 20-7	Customer name	Invoice number	Total £	VAT £	Net £
30 June	Upton Ltd	407	2,016	336	1,680
30 June	Bromyards	408	3,408	568	2,840
30 June	Kempsey & Co	409	4,272	712	3,560
30 June	Fernhill plc	410	2,448	408	2,040
	Totals		12,144	2,024	10,120

What will be the entries in the receivables ledger?

Select your account names from the following list: Bromyards, Discounts allowed, Discounts received, Fernhill plc, Kempsey & Co, Purchases, Payables ledger control, Purchases returns, Sales, Receivables ledger control, Sales returns, Upton Ltd, Value Added Tax.

Receivables ledger

Account name	Amount £	Debit	Credit

What will be the entries in the general ledger?

Select your account names from the following list: Discounts allowed, Discounts received, Purchases, Payables ledger control, Purchases returns, Sales, Receivables ledger control, Sales returns, Value Added Tax.

General ledger

Account name	Amount £	Debit	Credit

(b) The following credit transactions all took place on 30 June 20-7 and have been entered into the sales returns day book as shown below. No entries have yet been made in the ledgers.

Sales returns day book

Date 20-7	Customer name	Credit note number	Total £	VAT £	Net £
30 June	Drake & Co	CN 84	336	56	280
30 June	Hanbury Trading	CN 85	1,008	168	840
	Totals		1,344	224	1,120

What will be the entries in the receivables ledger?

Select your account names from the following list: Discounts allowed, Discounts received, Drake & Co, Hanbury Trading, Purchases, Payables ledger control, Purchases returns, Sales, Receivables ledger control, Sales returns, Value Added Tax.

Receivables ledger

Account name	Amount £	Debit	Credit

What will be the entries in the general ledger?

Select your account names from the following list: Discounts allowed, Discounts received, Purchases, Payables ledger control, Purchases returns, Sales, Receivables ledger control, Sales returns, Value Added Tax.

General ledger

Account name	Amount £	Debit	Credit

(c) The following discounts allowed transactions all took place on 30 June 20-7 and have been recorded in the discounts allowed day book as shown below. No entries have yet been made in the ledgers.

Discounts allowed day book

Date 20-7	Customer name	Credit note number	Total £	VAT £	Net £
30 June	Powick & Co	DA 58	30	5	25
30 June	Heath Trading	DA 59	42	7	35
	Totals		72	12	60

What will be the entries in the receivables ledger?

Select your account names from the following list: Discounts allowed, Discounts received, Heath Trading, Powick & Co, Purchases, Payables ledger control, Purchases returns, Sales, Receivables ledger control, Sales returns, Value Added Tax.

Receivables ledger

Account name	Amount £	Debit	Credit

What will be the entries in the general ledger?

Select your account names from the following list: Discounts allowed, Discounts received, Purchases, Payables ledger control, Purchases returns, Sales, Receivables ledger control, Sales returns, Value Added Tax.

General ledger

Account name	Amount £	Debit	Credit

4.8   These are the totals of the discounts allowed day book at the end of the month.

Discounts allowed day book

Customer name	Total £	VAT £	Net £
Totals	144	24	120

(a)   What will be the entries in the general ledger?

Select your account names from the following list: Discounts allowed, Discounts received, Purchases, Payables ledger control, Purchases returns, Sales, Receivables ledger control, Sales returns, VAT.

General ledger

Account name	Amount £	Debit	Credit

(b)   One of the entries in the discounts allowed day book is for a credit note sent to Khan Ltd for £55 plus VAT.

What will be the entry in the receivables ledger?

Select your account name from the following list: Discounts allowed, Discounts received, Khan Ltd, Purchases, Payables ledger control, Purchases returns, Sales, Receivables ledger control, Sales returns, VAT.

Receivables ledger

Account name	Amount £	Debit	Credit

4.9   You are the bookkeeper at Rankin Ltd.

Four sales invoices have been issued and have been partially entered in the analysed sales day book, shown below.

Complete the entries in the sales day book by inserting the appropriate details from each invoice, and then total the day book.

INVOICE NO 2132   30 June 20-4

From: Rankin Ltd

18 Blenheim Road

Linton

LT4 5JE

VAT Registration No 264 1432 55

To:	Hawke Ltd	
		£
	30 items of product T12 @ £10 each	300.00
	VAT @ 20%	60.00
	Total	360.00

INVOICE NO 2133   30 June 20-4

From: Rankin Ltd

18 Blenheim Road

Linton

LT4 5JE

VAT Registration No 264 1432 55

To:	T Martin	
		£
	25 items of product S12 @ £15 each	375.00
	VAT @ 20%	75.00
	Total	450.00

INVOICE NO 2134   30 June 20-4

From: Rankin Ltd

18 Blenheim Road

Linton

LT4 5JE

VAT Registration No 264 1432 55

To:	S Garner	
		£
	35 items of product S12 @ £15 each	525.00
	VAT @ 20%	105.00
	Total	630.00

INVOICE NO 2135   30 June 20-4

From: Rankin Ltd

18 Blenheim Road

Linton

LT4 5JE

VAT Registration No 264 1432 55

To:	JEC Ltd	
		£
	15 items of product T12 @ £10 each	150.00
	VAT @ 20%	30.00
	Total	180.00

Sales day book

Date 20-4	Customer name	Invoice number	Total £	VAT £	Net £	Product S12 £	Product T12 £
30 June	Hawke Ltd						
30 June	T Martin						
30 June	S Garner						
30 June	JEC Ltd						
	Totals						

4.10   You are the bookkeeper at Keylock Systems Ltd and have prepared the following invoice today, 10 June 20-3:

Keylock Systems Ltd
Invoice no: 35146

To: Locksafe & Co
Date: 10 June 20-3

	£
5 Triple A security locks @ £80 each	400.00
VAT @ 20%	80.00
TOTAL	480.00

Payment by BACS preferred

(a)   **You are to** record the invoice in the digital bookkeeping system by:
- selecting the correct daybook
- making the necessary entries

Daybook	✔
Sales day book	
Sales returns day book	
Purchases day book	
Discounts allowed day book	

Date 20-3	Name	Invoice number	Total £	VAT £	Net £

(b)   Identify the general ledger account into which the net amount will be entered.

Purchases: security locks	
Sales: security alarms	
Sales: security locks	
Sales returns: security locks	

(c)   Identify how the amount will be recorded in the general ledger account selected in (b).

As a debit entry	
As a credit entry	

4.11 This task is about totalling and balancing ledger accounts.

The following customer's account is in the receivables ledger at the close of the financial year on 31 May 20-9:

20-9	Details	Amount £	20-9	Details	Amount £
1 May	Balance b/f	1,834	15 May	Sales Returns	154
12 May	Sales	962	18 May	Bank	1,207
	Total			Total	

Complete the account by:
- inserting the balance carried down, together with date and details
- inserting the totals
- inserting the balance brought down together with date and details

Note:
- for details, choose from: Balance b/d, Balance c/d, Difference
- for date, choose from: 1 May, 31 May, 1 June, 30 June

4.12 This task is about transferring data from the books of prime entry.

The totals of the sales returns day book at the end of the month are as follows:

Details	Total £	VAT £	Net £
Total for month	504	84	420

(a) Show the entries to be made in the general ledger.

Account name	Amount £	Debit ✔	Credit ✔

An entry in the discounts allowed day book is for a credit note issued to Bingham Ltd for £25 plus VAT.

(b) Show the entry to be made in the receivables ledger.

Account name	Amount £	Debit ✔	Credit ✔

5 Process receipts from customers

5.1 A business receiving a remittance advice from a customer will need to check it against the sales documents. Which of the following checks is required?

Choose the correct option.

(a)	Sales documentation reference numbers	
(b)	The number of the cheque	
(c)	Bank account number	
(d)	Date of the remittance advice	

5.2 A business receiving a cheque from a customer in payment of an invoice will need to check it to make sure that it is in order. Which of the following list of checks is correct?

(a)	Date, signature, bank account number	
(b)	Date, signature, bank sort code	
(c)	Same amount in words and figures, in date, signature of customer	
(d)	Same amount in words and figures, in date, invoice number	

Which **one** of these options is correct?

5.3   The account shown below is in the receivables ledger of Johnston & Co. Also shown below is a BACS remittance advice received from R Romero at the end of August.

Date 20-4	Details	Amount £	Date 20-4	Details	Amount £
				R Romero	
1 Aug	Balance b/f	2,790	2 Aug	Bank	2,790
10 Aug	Sales invoice 392	690	26 June	Sales returns credit note 295	90
25 Aug	Sales Invoice 417	1,100			

R Romero

BACS REMITTANCE ADVICE

To: Johnston & Co   Date: 28 August 20-4

The following payment will be made direct to your bank.

Invoice number	Credit note number	Amount £
392		590
417		1,100
Total amount paid		1,690

You are required to check the remittance advice against the receivables ledger account.

State two discrepancies you can identify.

(a)

(b)

5.4   You are the bookkeeper at Sturt Trading and are processing customer transactions.

A receipt of £6,368 has been received from a credit customer, Coley Limited. The following is an extract for Coley Limited from your digital bookkeeping system, together with the remittance advice.

May sales list: Coley Ltd		
Date 20-6	**Details**	**Amount £**
4 May	Invoice 5207	2,385
10 May	Credit note 84	−65
12 May	Invoice 5314	1,459
22 May	Credit note 91	−112
29 May	Invoice 5465	2,671

Remittance Advice: Coley Ltd
To: Sturt Trading
31 May 20-6

Date 20-6	**Details**	**Amount £**
4 May	Invoice 5270	2,385
10 May	Credit note 84	65
21 May	Invoice 5314	1,459
22 May	Credit note 91	−212
29 May	Invoice 5465	2,671
TOTAL: Paid by BACS 31 May		6,368

(a)   **You are to** identify the discrepancies (if any) between the transactions from the sales list and the transactions in the remittance advice.

20-6	**Details**	**£**	**Discrepancies**
4 May	Invoice 5207	2,385	
10 May	Credit note 84	−65	
12 May	Invoice 5314	1,459	
22 May	Credit note 91	−112	
29 May	Invoice 5465	2,671	

For the discrepancies column, choose from the following options (use each once only):

No discrepancy
Incorrect date
Incorrect invoice number
Incorrectly recorded
Incorrect amount

(b)   What will be the balance of Coley Limited's account after the payment of £6,368 has been allocated to its account?

Balance of Coley Ltd's trade receivables account	**✔**
(a) £100 underpaid	
(b) £100 overpaid	
(c) £30 underpaid	
(d) £30 overpaid	

(c) An invoice to supply goods for £5,232 including VAT has been sent to Goranz Limited offering prompt payment discount of 2.5% for payment within seven days.

What will be the amount payable by Goranz Limited if it pays within seven days?

£ [   ]

(d) The following remittance advice has been received by Sturt Trading from Mohan & Co:

Mohan & Co
BACS remittance advice
To: Sturt Trading
Date: 31 May 20-6
Amount: £2,250
Detail:
- £1,450 part payment of balance at 1 May 20-6
- £800 part payment of invoice 5332
- Full allocation of credit note 102 to invoice 5332

You are to show the outstanding amount for each entry after the remittance has been allocated.

Date 20-6	Detail	£	Outstanding amount £
1 May	Opening balance	2,450	
14 May	Invoice 5332	1,576	
26 May	Credit note 102	–338	

6 Financial documents for purchases

6.1 When a credit note is received by the buyer in respect of faulty goods returned by the buyer, it should be checked against the details on the:

(a) Invoice	
(b) Delivery note	
(c) Remittance advice	

Which **one** of these options is correct?

6.2 A business will use supplier codes to refer to accounts in:

(a) The general ledger	
(b) The receivables ledger	
(c) The payables ledger	

Which **one** of these options is correct?

6.3 A business will use general ledger codes to refer to accounts for:

(a) Purchases	
(b) Suppliers	
(c) Customers	

Which **one** of these options is correct?

6.4   A supply of office chairs has been delivered to Praxis Stationery. Praxis Stationery completes a Goods Received Note as shown below.

Examine the note and answer the questions below by selecting the correct words from the following list:

Praxis Stationery	**2 chairs missing**	**2 chairs damaged**	**purchases day book**
credit note	**Helicon Furniture**	**debit note**	**sales day book**
receivables ledger	**returns note**	**refund note**	**payables ledger**

GOODS RECEIVED NOTE
PRAXIS STATIONERY

GRN no.   302

supplier   Helicon Furniture

date   4 December 20-4

order ref.	quantity	description
8246	10	Office chairs (Code Typ72652)

received by.........*D Nutt*..................... checked by ....*N Mason*............

condition of goods   condition – *good (8 chairs)*
                                    damages – *2 chairs damaged*
                                    shortages *none*

(a)   Who has supplied the chairs?

(b)   What is the problem with the consignment?

(c)   What document would be issued by the supplier to adjust the account of Praxis Stationery?

(d)   Where in the supplier's accounting records would the account of Praxis Stationery be maintained?

6.5   A supply of office chairs has been delivered to Praxis Stationery by Firth Furniture. The purchase order sent from Praxis Stationery, and the invoice from Firth Furniture, are shown below.

PURCHASE ORDER
PRAXIS STATIONERY

No 1066
Date 10 08 20-3

45 Jarvis Street, Mereford MR1 2GH

To: Firth Furniture

Please supply 12 Executive office chairs (product code EXCH45)

Purchase price: £150 each, plus VAT @ 20%

Discount: less 20% trade discount, as agreed

INVOICE
FIRTH FURNITURE
17 Chippendale Street
Lesspool LP1 5HG
VAT Reg 171 7326 11

To:
Praxis Stationery
45 Jarvis Street, Mereford MR1 2GH

Date 11 08 20-3
No. 6518
Account PS6232

Quantity	Product code	Price (£)	Total (£)	Net (£)	VAT (£)	Total (£)
12	EXCH45	150.00	1,800.00	1,620.00	324.00	1,944.00

Check the invoice against the purchase order and answer the following questions:

Has the correct purchase price of the chairs been charged? Yes or No?	
Has the correct discount been applied? Yes or No?	
What would be the VAT amount charged if the invoice was correct?	£
What would be the total amount charged if the invoice was correct?	£

6.6   A supply of office desks has been delivered to Praxis Stationery by Firth Furniture. The purchase order sent from Praxis Stationery, and the delivery note from Firth Furniture, are shown below.

PURCHASE ORDER   **No** 1261
PRAXIS STATIONERY   **Date** 05 09 20-3

45 Jarvis Street, Mereford MR1 2GH

To: Firth Furniture

Please supply 4 oak finish office tables (product code OTT28).

Purchase price: £80 each, plus VAT @ 20%.

Discount: less 20% trade discount, as agreed.

DELIVERY NOTE
FIRTH FURNITURE
17 Chippendale Street
Lesspool LP1 5HG
VAT Reg 171 7326 11

To: Date 10 09 20-3
Praxis Stationery   No. 6610
45 Jarvis Street, Mereford MR1 2GH   Account PS6232

Quantity	Product code	Description
5	OTT28	Office tables, oak finish (product code OTT28) @ £80 each, less trade discount @ 20%, plus VAT @ 20%.

Check the delivery note against the purchase order and answer the following questions:

Has the correct number of tables been supplied? Yes or No?	
Has the correct type of table been supplied? Yes or No?	
What will be the total of the invoice on the basis of the details on the delivery note?	£
If a credit note were issued, what would be the total, including VAT?	£

6.7   Identify which document would be used by a buyer for each of the purposes below.

Purpose	Document
Information from the supplier regarding the goods or services required	
Issued to the supplier stating the goods or services requested	
Used by the buyer to record receipt of goods	
Sent to the supplier with faulty goods	

For the documents, choose from the following options (use each once only):

Price enquiry
Goods returned note
Purchase order
Goods received note

6.8   You are the bookkeeper at Reaves Traders Limited. The following documents relate to incorrect goods supplied by Ostrowski Limited.

Reaves Traders Ltd
Goods Returns Note
To: Ostrowski Ltd
5 June 20-2
12 x Product 93
Returned as faulty
£20 net each
Credit requested

Ostrowski Ltd		
Credit note: CN102		
To: Greaves Trading Ltd		
Date: 5 July 20-2		
		£
21 x Product 93		420.00
VAT @ 20%		84.00
Total		504.00

Identify **three** discrepancies in the credit note:

Discrepancy	✔
Buyer details	
Quantity of goods	
Date of credit note	
Net amount	
VAT amount	
Total amount	

7 Accounting for purchases, returns and discounts

7.1 Which **one** of the following is a financial document?

(a)	Purchases invoice	
(b)	Account of T Lewis in the payables ledger	
(c)	Purchases day book	
(d)	Payables ledger control account	

7.2 Which **one** of the following is in the right order?

(a)	Purchases day book; payables ledger control account; invoice received; purchases account; VAT account; supplier's account	
(b)	Purchases account; VAT account; supplier's account; payables ledger control account; purchases day book; invoice received	
(c)	Invoice received; purchases day book; purchases account; VAT account; payables ledger control account; supplier's account	
(d)	Invoice received; purchases account; VAT account; payables ledger control account; supplier's account; purchases day book	

7.3 Which **one** of the following shows the correct general ledger entries to record the purchase of goods for resale on credit?

(a)	Debit payables ledger control; debit VAT; credit purchases	
(b)	Debit payables ledger control; credit purchases; credit VAT	
(c)	Debit purchases; debit VAT; credit payables ledger control	
(d)	Debit purchases; credit payables ledger control; credit VAT	

For Activities 7.4 and 7.5:

- work in pounds and pence, where appropriate

- the rate of Value Added Tax is to be calculated at 20% (when calculating VAT amounts, you should ignore fractions of a penny, ie round down to a whole penny)

- use a coding system incorporating the following:

purchases day book	*– PDB55*	*general ledger account numbers*	
purchases returns day book	*– PRDB14*	*payables ledger control account*	*– GL2350*
		purchases account	*– GL5100*
payables ledger account numbers		*purchases returns account*	*– GL5110*
S Burston	*– PL530*	*Value Added Tax account*	*– GL2200*
Iley Supplies Ltd	*– PL605*		
Malvern Manufacturing	*– PL625*		
SG Enterprises	*– PL720*		

7.4 Wyvern Products Limited manufactures and sells garden furniture. During May 20-2 the following credit transactions took place:

20-2

3 May	Purchased goods from Malvern Manufacturing £170 + VAT, invoice no 7321
9 May	Purchased goods from S Burston £265 + VAT, invoice no SB745
12 May	Purchased goods from Iley Supplies Ltd £450 + VAT, invoice no 4721
18 May	Purchased goods from SG Enterprises £825 + VAT, invoice no 3947
23 May	Purchased goods from S Burston £427 + VAT, invoice no SB773
30 May	Purchased goods from Malvern Manufacturing £364 + VAT, invoice no 7408

You are to:

(a) Enter the above transactions in Wyvern Products Limited's purchases day book for May 20-2, using the format shown on the next page.

(b) Record the accounting entries in Wyvern Products Limited's general ledger and payables ledger. (You will need to retain the ledger accounts for use with Activity 7.5.)

Purchases Day Book						PDB55
Date	Supplier name	Invoice number	Account code	Total £	VAT £	Net £

7.5 The following are the purchases returns of Wyvern Products Limited for May 20-2. They are to be:

(a) Recorded in the purchases returns day book for May 20-2, using the format shown on the next page.

(b) Recorded in the general ledger and payables ledger (use the ledgers already prepared in the answer to Activity 7.4).

20-2

11 May Returned goods to Malvern Manufacturing £70 + VAT, credit note no CN345 received

17 May Returned goods to Iley Supplies Ltd £85 + VAT, credit note no CN241 received

24 May Returned goods to SG Enterprises £25 + VAT, credit note no 85 received

31 May Returned goods to S Burston £55 + VAT, credit note no SB95 received

Purchases Returns Day Book						PRDB14
Date	Supplier name	Credit note number	Account code	Total £	VAT £	Net £

7.6   Purchases invoices have been prepared and partially recorded in the purchases day book, as shown below.

(a)   Complete the entries in the purchases day book by inserting the appropriate figures for each invoice.

(b)   Total the last five columns of the purchases day book.

Purchases day book

Date 20-4	Supplier name	Invoice number	Total £	VAT £	Net £	Purchases type 1 £	Purchases type 2 £
30 June	King & Co	K641	2,016		1,680		1,680
30 June	Rossingtons	2129		512		2,560	
30 June	Moniz Ltd	M/149	2,208				1,840
	Totals						

7.7 You are employed by Churchtown Limited as an Accounts Assistant. The business has a manual accounting system. Double-entry takes place in the general ledger; individual accounts of trade payables are kept as subsidiary accounts in the payables ledger. The VAT rate is 20%.

Notes:

- show your answer with a tick, words or figures, as appropriate

- coding is not required

(a) The following credit transactions all took place on 30 June 20-8 and have been recorded in the purchases day book as shown below. No entries have yet been made in the ledgers.

Purchases day book

Date 20-8	Supplier name	Invoice number	Total £	VAT £	Net £
30 June	H & L Ltd	5986	6,528	1,088	5,440
30 June	Sperrin & Co	P864	2,208	368	1,840
30 June	Hickmores	H591	4,608	768	3,840
30 June	Marklew plc	6417	1,104	184	920
	Totals		14,448	2,408	12,040

What will be the entries in the payables ledger?

Select your account names from the following list: Discounts allowed, Discounts received, H & L Ltd, Hickmores, Marklew plc, Purchases, Payables ledger control, Purchases returns, Sales, Receivables ledger control, Sales returns, Sperrin & Co, Value Added Tax.

Payables ledger

Account name	Amount £	Debit	Credit

What will be the entries in the general ledger?

Select your account names from the following list: Discounts allowed, Discounts received, Purchases, Payables ledger control, Purchases returns, Sales, Receivables ledger control, Sales returns, Value Added Tax.

General ledger

Account name	Amount £	Debit	Credit

(b)   The following credit transactions all took place on 30 June 20-8 and have been entered into the purchases returns day book as shown below. No entries have yet been made in the ledgers.

Purchases returns day book

Date 20-8	Supplier name	Credit note number	Total £	VAT £	Net £
30 June	Marcer Transport	564	624	104	520
30 June	Schuller Ltd	CN28	432	72	360
	Totals		1,056	176	880

What will be the entries in the payables ledger?

Select your account names from the following list: Discounts allowed, Discounts received, Marcer Transport, Purchases, Payables ledger control, Purchases returns, Sales, Receivables ledger control, Sales returns, Schuller Ltd, Value Added Tax.

Payables ledger

Account name	Amount £	Debit	Credit

What will be the entries in the general ledger?

Select your account names from the following list: Discounts allowed, Discounts received, Purchases, Payables ledger control, Purchases returns, Sales, Receivables ledger control, Sales returns, Value Added Tax.

General ledger

Account name	Amount £	Debit	Credit

(c)   The following discounts received transactions all took place on 30 June 20-8 and have been recorded in the discounts received day book as shown below. No entries have yet been made in the ledgers.

Discounts received day book

Date 20-8	Supplier name	Credit note number	Total £	VAT £	Net £
30 June	DDE & Co	CN141	18	3	15
30 June	Transpo Ltd	CN28	24	4	20
	Totals		42	7	35

What will be the entries in the payables ledger?

Select your account names from the following list: DDE & Co, Discounts allowed, Discounts received, Purchases, Payables ledger control, Purchases returns, Sales, Receivables ledger control, Sales returns, Transpo Ltd, Value Added Tax.

Payables ledger

Account name	Amount £	Debit	Credit

What will be the entries in the general ledger?

Select your account names from the following list: Discounts allowed, Discounts received, Purchases, Payables ledger control, Purchases returns, Sales, Receivables ledger control, Sales returns, Value Added Tax.

General ledger

Account name	Amount £	Debit	Credit

7.8 These are the totals of the discounts received day book at the end of the month.

Discounts received day book

Supplier name	Total £	VAT £	Net £
Totals	234	39	195

(a) What will be the entries in the general ledger?

Select your account names from the following list: Discounts allowed, Discounts received, Purchases, Payables ledger control, Purchases returns, Sales, Receivables ledger control, Sales returns, VAT.

General ledger

Account name	Amount £	Debit	Credit

(b) One of the entries in the discounts received day book is for a credit note received from Hussain plc for £85 plus VAT.

What will be the entry in the payables ledger?

Select your account name from the following list: Discounts allowed, Discounts received, Hussain plc, Purchases, Payables ledger control, Purchases returns, Sales, Receivables ledger control, Sales returns, VAT.

Payables ledger

Account name	Amount £	Debit	Credit

7.9   You are the bookkeeper at Rankin Ltd.

Four purchases invoices have been received and have been partially recorded in the analysed purchases day book, shown below.

Complete the entries in the purchases day book by inserting the appropriate details from each invoice, and then total the day book.

INVOICE NO 4681	30 June 20-4

From: Lyster Ltd
    44 Mill Street
    Linton
    LT3 6AJ
    VAT Registration No 451 3268 01

To:	Rankin Ltd	
		£
	100 items of product S12 @ £10 each	1,000.00
	VAT @ 20%	200.00
	Total	1,200.00

INVOICE NO 6234	30 June 20-4

From: T England
    14 Nelson Street
    Westerham
    WH6 9JK
    VAT Registration No 323 8614 25

To:	Rankin Ltd	
		£
	60 items of product T12 @ £6 each	360.00
	VAT @ 20%	72.00
	Total	432.00

INVOICE NO 1634   30 June 20-4

From: Mere Ltd

      22 Moreton Road

      Ruddington

      RT5 2BN

      VAT Registration No 495 0232 55

To: Rankin Ltd

	£
150 items of product T12 @ £6 each	900.00
VAT @ 20%	180.00
Total	1,080.00

INVOICE NO 8561   30 June 20-4

From: J Mehta

      84 The High Road

      Linton

      LT1 2DS

      VAT Registration No 264 9781 65

To: Rankin Ltd

	£
40 items of product S12 @ £10 each	400.00
VAT @ 20%	80.00
Total	480.00

Purchases day book

Date 20-4	Supplier name	Invoice number	Total £	VAT £	Net £	Product S12 £	Product T12 £
30 June	Lyster Ltd						
30 June	T England						
30 June	Mere Ltd						
30 June	J Mehta						
	Totals						

7.10 You are the bookkeeper at Beeches Care Home and are processing supplier invoices. The following invoice has been received:

PPE Supplies
Invoice no: 45761

To: Beeches Care Home
Date: 29 May 20-7

	£
12 packs of face masks at £15.50 each	186.00
VAT @ 20%	37.20
TOTAL	223.20

Payment by BACS preferred

(a) **You are to** record the invoice in the bookkeeping system by:

- selecting the correct daybook

- making the appropriate entries on the available line in the day book

- totalling the total, VAT and net columns

Daybook	✔
Sales day book	
Purchases returns day book	
Purchases day book	
Discounts received day book	

Date 20-7	Name	Invoice number	Total £	VAT £	Net £
2 May	Linen Traders	3690	542.62	90.44	452.18
10 May	GoodFood Ltd	74/GF	718.04	119.67	598.37
15 May	PPE Supplies	45417	374.70	62.45	312.25
23 May	Fruit 'n Veg Ltd	1974	475.32	79.22	396.10
	TOTALS				

(b)   Identify how the total amount you have calculated for the total column will be recorded in the general ledger.

	✔
As a debit entry to receivables ledger control account	
As a debit entry to payables ledger control account	
As a credit entry to receivables ledger control account	
As a credit entry to payables ledger control account	

(c)   Identify how the total of the VAT column will be recorded in the general ledger account for VAT.

	✔
As a debit entry	
As a credit entry	

7.11   This task is about transferring data from the books of prime entry.

The totals of the purchases day book at the end of the month are as follows:

Details	Total £	VAT £	Net £
Total for month	7,344	1,224	6,120

(a)   Show the entries to be made in the general ledger.

Account name	Amount £	Debit ✔	Credit ✔

An entry in the discounts received day book is for a credit note received from Carlton Ltd for £20 plus VAT.

(b)   Show the entry in the payables ledger.

Account name	Amount £	Debit ✔	Credit ✔

7.12   This task is about totalling and balancing ledger accounts.

The following supplier's account is in the payables ledger at the close of the financial year on 30 June 20-6:

20-6	Details	Amount £	20-6	Details	Amount £
5 June	Purchases Returns	174	1 June	Balance b/f	3,054
25 June	Bank	2,562	20 June	Purchases	1,526
	Total			Total	

Complete the account by:

- inserting the balance carried down, together with date and details

- inserting the totals

- inserting the balance brought down together with date and details

Note:

- for details, choose from: Balance b/d, Balance c/d, Difference

- for date, choose from: 1 June, 30 June, 1 July, 31 July

8 Process payments to suppliers

8.1 If a supplier duplicates an invoice for goods ordered, the likely effect will be:

(a) An increase in the total amount owing shown on the statement of account	
(b) A decrease in the total amount owing shown on the statement of account	
(c) No effect at all	

Which **one** of these options is correct?

8.2 A remittance advice is likely to show details of the following financial documents issued:

(a) Purchase invoices, purchase credit notes, goods received notes	
(b) Purchase invoices, purchase credit notes, payments made	
(c) Purchase invoices, purchase credit notes, total amount owing	

Which **one** of these options is correct?

8.3 The payables ledger account of a supplier shows a purchase invoice which is not shown on the supplier's statement of account. This:

(a) Can be adjusted by asking the supplier to issue a credit note	
(b) Will reduce the total amount shown as owing on the statement of account	
(c) Will increase the total amount shown as owing on the statement of account	

Which **one** of these options is correct?

8.4   Shown below is a statement of account received from Masters Supplies, a credit supplier, and the supplier's account as shown in the payables ledger of Broadfield Traders.

Masters Supplies

21 HighStreet, East Mereford, MR7 9HJ

To: Broadfield Traders

Unit 18 Elgar Estate

Mereford, MR2 5FG   STATEMENT OF ACCOUNT

Date 20-4	Invoice Number	Details	Invoice Amount £	Payment Amount £	Balance £
1 May	699	Goods	2,000		2,000
5 May	712	Goods	1,100		3,100
9 May	731	Goods	750		3,850
28 May	790	Goods	1,360		5,210
1 June	-	Payment		3,850	1,360

	Masters Supplies				
Date 20-4	Details	Amount £	Date 20-4	Details	Amount £
1 June	Bank	3,850	1 May	Purchases	2,000
28 June	Bank	1,000	8 May	Purchases	1,100
			10 May	Purchases	750

(a)   Which item is missing from the statement of account from Masters Supplies? Select your answer from the following list:

Invoice 699, Invoice 712, Invoice 731, Invoice 790, Payment for £3,850, Payment for £1,000

(b)   Which item is missing from the supplier account in Broadfield Traders' payables ledger? Select your answer from the following list:

Invoice 699, Invoice 712, Invoice 731, Invoice 790, Payment for £3,850, Payment for £1,000

(c)   Assuming any differences between the statement of account from Masters Supplies and the supplier account in Broadfield Traders' payables ledger are simply due to omission errors, what is the amount owing to Masters Supplies?

£

8.5 Mereford Traders sends BACS remittance advice notes to suppliers on the last day of the month following the month of invoice. Mereford Traders banks with National Bank plc, and A Strauss & Co banks with Mercia Bank plc. Below is an uncompleted BACS remittance advice and an extract from Mereford Traders' payables ledger.

Mereford Traders		
45 College Street		
Mereford, MR3 4GT		
BACS REMITTANCE ADVICE		
To:	Date:	
The following payment will be made direct to your bank.		
Invoice number	**Credit note number**	**Amount** £
	Total amount paid	

A Strauss & Co					
Date 20-4	**Details**	**Amount** £	**Date** 20-4	**Details**	**Amount** £
3 Feb	Purchases returns credit note CN101	400	15 Feb	Purchases Invoice 2250	1,750
20 Mar	Purchases returns credit note CN105	300	12 Mar	Purchases Invoice 2461	2,340
31 Mar	Bank	1,350	29 Mar	Purchases Invoice 2479	1,600
			10 Apr	Purchases Invoice 2499	2,107

(a) The BACS remittance advice will be sent:

(a)	With a cheque to Mereford Traders	
(b)	Without a cheque to A Strauss & Co	
(c)	To Mercia Bank plc with a cheque	
(d)	To Mercia Bank plc without a cheque	

Which **one** of these options is correct?

(b)   What will be the date shown on the BACS remittance advice?

(a)	28 February	
(b)	31 March	
(c)	30 April	
(d)	31 May	

Which **one** of these options is correct?

(c)   What will be the items shown on the BACS remittance advice?

(a)	Invoice 2250, Invoice 2461, invoice 2479, invoice 2687	
(b)	Invoice 2461, invoice 2479, credit note CN105	
(c)	Invoice 2250, Invoice 2461, invoice 2479, credit note CN101	
(d)	Invoice 2250, Invoice 2461, credit note CN101, credit note CN105	

Which **one** of these options is correct?

(d)   The amount of the remittance advice will be:

(a)	£3,390	
(b)	£4,990	
(c)	£3,640	
(d)	£5,390	

Which **one** of these options is correct?

8.6 You are the bookkeeper at Pierson Limited. It is the policy of Pierson Limited to check statements of account when they are received and to include in the payment only those transactions from the statement that are shown in the supplier's account in payables ledger.

The following is the supplier account activity from the digital bookkeeping system for Killeen & Co:

Supplier activity report: Killeen & Co			
Date 20-8	Details	Debit £	Credit £
1 June	Balance b/f		5,026
3 June	Credit note CN 62	125	
10 June	Bank payment	5,026	
15 June	Invoice 5205		2,109
17 June	Invoice 5232		1,095
26 June	Invoice 5417		822

(a) The statement of account from the supplier is below. **You are to** identify the **three** items in the statement of account that should not be included in the payment because they are missing from the supplier activity report.

Killeen & Co **Park Road, Patchling, PG1 2DP** **STATEMENT OF ACCOUNT:** Pierson Ltd				
Date 20-8	Document number	Details	Amount £	✔
3 June	CN 62	Goods returned	−125	
15 June	5205	Goods	2,109	
17 June	5232	Goods	1,095	
20 June	5302	Goods	1,746	
26 June	5417	Goods	822	
29 June	CN 75	Goods returned	−268	
30 June	5519	Goods	2,312	

(b) Payment to Killeen & Co will be made on 6 July 20-8.

Complete the remittance advice, below, for the payment.

Pierson Ltd **BACS Remittance Advice** To:		
Date	Your reference	Amount £
	TOTAL	

8.7   You are the bookkeeper at Peart Limited. A statement of account for April 20-7 has been received from a supplier, Jukes Limited.

The following is an extract from your digital bookkeeping system of the April purchases from Jukes Limited and its statement of account:

April purchases list: Jukes Ltd

Date 20-4	Details	Amount £
2 April	Invoice 6318	1,890
5 April	Credit note 422	−75
16 April	Invoice 6765	2,230
22 April	Credit note 438	−212
25 April	Invoice 6821	1,435

Statement of account: Jukes Ltd
To: Peart Ltd
30 April 20-4

Date 20-4	Details	Amount £
2 April	Invoice 6318	1,990
15 April	Credit note 422	−75
16 April	Invoice 7656	2,230
25 April	Invoice 6821	1,435
	TOTAL	5,580

You are to identify the discrepancies (if any) between the transactions from the purchases list and the transactions on the statement of account.

20-4	Details	£	Discrepancies
2 April	Invoice 6318	1,890	
5 April	Credit note 422	−75	
16 April	Invoice 6765	2,230	
22 April	Credit note 438	−212	
25 April	Invoice 6821	1,435	

For the discrepancies column, choose from the following options (use each once only):

No discrepancy
Incorrect amount
Not on statement
Incorrect date
Incorrect invoice number

9 Cash book

9.1 Which **one** of the following transactions will be recorded on the receipts side of cash book?

(a)	Bank charges for £55	
(b)	Payment of VAT to HM Revenue & Customs for £1,820	
(c)	BACS transfer from a trade receivable for £1,950	
(d)	Drawings made by the owner of the business for £750	

9.2 The following transactions all took place on 30 June and have been recorded on the debit side of the cash book of Jane Martin, as shown below. No entries have yet been made in the ledgers.

Note that Jane Martin's business is not registered for Value Added Tax.

Cash book – debit side

Date 20-4	Details	Cash £	Bank £
30 June	Balance b/f		2,076
30 June	Delta & Co		325
30 June	Boscawen Ltd		1,540

(a) What will be the entries in the receivables ledger?

Select your account names from the following list: Balance b/f, Bank, Boscawen Ltd, Delta & Co, Payables ledger control, Receivables ledger control.

Receivables ledger

Account name	Amount £	Debit	Credit

(b)   What will be the entries in the general ledger?

Select your account names from the following list: Balance b/f, Bank, Boscawen Ltd, Delta & Co, Payables ledger control, Receivables ledger control.

General ledger

Account name	Amount £	Debit	Credit

The following transactions all took place on 30 June and have been recorded on the credit side of the cash book of Jane Martin, as shown below. No entries have yet been made in the ledgers.

Cash book – credit side

Date 20-4	Details	Cash £	Bank £
30 June	Wages	1,265	
30 June	Office equipment		1,968

(c)   What will be the entries in the general ledger?

Select your account name from the following list: Bank, Office equipment, Payables ledger control, Receivables ledger control, Wages.

General ledger

Account name	Amount £	Debit	Credit

9.3 The following transactions all took place on 30 June 20-4 and have been recorded in the cash book of Rafe Sadler, as shown below. No entries have yet been made in the ledgers.

Note that Rafe Sadler's business is not registered for Value Added Tax.

Dr				Cash Book			CB73 Cr
Date	Details	Cash	Bank	Date	Details	Cash	Bank
20-4		£	£	20-4		£	£
30 Jun	Balances b/f	250	3,840	30 Jun	Wages		1,175
30 Jun	Smithsons Ltd			30 Jun	Rent		1,200
	(trade receivable)		2,325	30 Jun	Stationery	120	
30 Jun	Egerton & Co			30 Jun	Balances c/d	130	4,215
	(trade receivable)		425				
		250	6,590			250	6,590
1 Jul	Balances b/d	130	4,215				

(a) What will be the entries in the receivables ledger?

Select your account names from the following list: Balance b/f, Bank, Egerton & Co, Payables ledger control, Receivables ledger control, Smithsons Ltd.

Receivables ledger

Account name	Amount £	Debit	Credit

(b) What will be the entries in the general ledger?

Select your account names from the following list: Balance b/f, Bank, Payables ledger control, Rent, Receivables ledger control, Stationery, Smithsons Ltd, Wages.

General ledger

Account name	Amount £	Debit	Credit

9.4 The following cash book shows a number of transactions of Wentworths which all took place on 30 September 20-1:

Dr					Cash Book					CB68 Cr	
Date	Details	Account code	Cash	Bank	Date	Details	Account code	Cash	Bank
20-1			£	£	20-1			£	£
30 Sep	Balances b/f		644	3,045	30 Sep	Nelson Stores (trade payable)			1,940
30 Sep	Cash sales		88		30 Sep	Cash purchases			192
30 Sep	Albany Ltd (trade receivable)			1,580	30 Sep	General expenses		128	
30 Sep	Balance c/d			201	30 Sep	Wages			1,254
					30 Sep	Office equipment			1,440
					30 Sep	Balance c/d		604	
			732	4,826				732	4,826
1 Oct	Balance b/d		604		1 Oct	Balance b/d			201

(a) The bank balance brought forward of £3,045 on 30 September shows that, according to the cash book, the business has money in the bank. True or false?

(b) The bank balance brought down of £201 on 1 October shows that, according to the cash book, the business has money in the bank. True or false?

(c) You are to transfer the data from the cash book into the general ledger of Wentworths. Note that a bank account is not required.

(d) Show the entries in the receivables ledger and payables ledger of Wentworths.

Note: Wentworth's business is not registered for Value Added Tax.

9.5 The balances in Sally Henshaw's cash book at 3 August 20-7 were as follows:

	£
Cash in hand	286
Bank overdraft	3,472

The following transactions took place:

3 Aug	Paid rent by cheque £760
4 Aug	Sales £334, cash received
5 Aug	Received a cheque of £1,475 from Murphy Ltd in full settlement of a debt of £1,490
8 Aug	Paid rates by direct debit £223
8 Aug	Paid JJ Supplies by cheque £490 after deducting £10 prompt payment discount
10 Aug	Drawings, £400 by cheque, made by Sally Henshaw
10 Aug	Paid wages £480 in cash

Required:

• Record the above transactions in the cash book on the next page.

• Balance the cash and bank columns at 10 August 20-7, and bring the balances down on 11 August 20-7.

Note: Sally Henshaw's business is not registered for Value Added Tax.

Cash Book

Dr

Date 20-7	Details	Cash £	Bank £

Cr

Date 20-7	Details	Cash £	Bank £

9.6   Emma Maxwell uses a cash book as part of her double-entry bookkeeping system. The following details relate to March 20-3.

March		£
1	Balance of cash	200
	Overdrawn bank balance	1,898
2	Bank payment made to Lindum Supplies in settlement of an invoice for £260	254
6	Cheque from Court Ltd paid into bank	1,236
11	Paid rent by cheque	550
13	BACS transfer received from H Sweeney. Prompt payment discount of £10 has been taken by the customer	1,696
14	Sales, cash received	639
23	Paid wages in cash	655
24	Sales, cash received	786
26	Standing order to Wyvern Council	195
27	Interest charged by bank	45
28	BACS transfer received from Mills and Co Ltd	477

Required:

- Record the above transactions in the cash book shown on the next page.

- Balance the cash book at the end of the month and bring down the balances at 1 April 20-3.

Note: Emma Maxwell's business is not registered for Value Added Tax.

Cash Book

Dr

Date 20-3	Details	Cash £	Bank £	Date 20-3	Details	Cash £	Bank £

Cr

9.7   Which **one** of the following transactions will be recorded on the payments side of cash book?

(a)	Repayment of VAT by HM Revenue & Customs for £255	
(b)	BACS transfer from a trade receivable for £690	
(c)	Debit card payment to a trade payable for £940	
(d)	Increase in owner's capital by bank transfer for £5,000	

9.8   Show whether the following statements are true or false.

Statement		True	False
(a)	Cash and bank accounts are the general ledger accounts when cash book is used as a book of prime entry only		
(b)	The payables ledger column total from cash book is credited to payables ledger control account in general ledger		
(c)	The trade payables column total from an analysed cash book is debited to payables ledger control account in general ledger		
(d)	The VAT column total on the payments side of cash book is debited to VAT account in general ledger		

9.9 You are an accounts assistant at Denison Limited. One of your duties is to write up the cash book.

There are five payments to be recorded in Denison Limited's cash book.

Receipts for cash payments

Received cash with thanks for goods bought.	Received cash with thanks for goods bought.
From Denison Ltd, a customer without a credit account.	From Denison Ltd, a customer without a credit account.
Net £40	Net £160
VAT £8	VAT £32
Total £48	Total £192
Clark & Co	*T Kinnear*

Bank payments

Gaskin Ltd	Bristow Stationery	Roussouw & Co
(Payables ledger account PL110)	(No credit account with this supplier)	(Payables ledger account PL280)
£1,690	£144 including VAT	£1,140

(a) Record the details from the two receipts for cash payments and the three bank payments into the credit side of the cash book shown below and total each column.

Cash book – credit side

Details	Cash £	Bank £	VAT £	Trade payables £	Cash purchases £	Stationery expenses £
Balance b/f						
Clark & Co						
T Kinnear						
Gaskin Ltd						
Bristow Stationery						
Roussouw & Co						
Totals						

There are two bank receipts from credit customers to be recorded in Denison Limited's cash book:

Passmores   £455

S McNulty   £833

(b) Record the above details into the debit side of the cash book and total each column.

Cash book – debit side

Details	Cash £	Bank £	Trade receivables £
Balance b/f	642	1,022	
Passmores			
S McNulty			
Totals			

(c) Using your answers to (a) and (b) above, calculate the cash balance.

£ [   ]

(d) Using your answers to (a) and (b) above, calculate the bank balance.

£ [   ]

(e) Will the bank balance calculated in (d) above be a debit or credit balance?

Debit	
Credit	

9.10 There are four payments to be recorded in Rowson Limited's cash book.

Payments to suppliers who do not offer credit accounts:

- cash paid to Mary Wallbank of £192, including VAT, for goods purchased

- a bank payment of £425, no VAT, to Wenton Council for rates

Payments to credit suppliers:

- BACS payments made as authorised on the two invoices shown below

Sanders plc 2 Albany Road Wenton WT4 8PQ VAT Registration No 208 7641 00

Invoice No. 6231	30 June 20-4

To: Rowson Ltd
          14 Blenheim Road
          Wenton, WT2 1XJ	

	£
50 items of AB @ £10.00 each	500.00
VAT @ 20%	100.00
Total	600.00

Authorised for payment in full: T Rowson

Terms: 30 days net.

J Panas Market Street South Wenton WT6 4JK VAT Registration No 396 4918 00

Invoice No. I2721	30 June 20-4

To: Rowson Ltd
          14 Blenheim Road
          Wenton, WT2 1XJ	

	£
80 items of AD @ £7.00 each	560.00
VAT @ 20%	112.00
Total	672.00

Authorised for payment in full: T Rowson

Terms: 30 days net.

(a) Record the details of the four payments into the credit side of the cash book shown below and total each column.

Cash book – credit side

Details	Cash	Bank	VAT	Trade payables	Cash purchases	Other expenses
	£	£	£	£	£	£
Balance b/f		2,417				
Totals						

There are three amounts received to be recorded in Rowson Limited's cash book.

Cheques received from credit customers:

- LFJ plc £1,685

- Wragg Ltd £2,135

Cash received:

- £200 received from Nikki Shah for rent of office space (No VAT)

(b) Record the details of the three receipts into the debit side of the cash book shown below and total each column.

Cash book – debit side

Details	Cash	Bank	Trade receivables	Other income
	£	£	£	£
Balance b/f	208			
Totals				

(c)   Using your answers to (a) and (b) on the previous page, calculate the cash balance.

£ [   ]

(d)   Using your answers to (a) and (b) on the previous page, calculate the bank balance. If your calculations show that the bank account is overdrawn your answer should start with a minus sign.

£ [   ]

(e)   What will be the entry in Wragg Ltd's account in the receivables ledger to record the payment received?

Receivables ledger

Account name	Amount £	Debit	Credit
Wragg Ltd			

9.11   You are the bookkeeper at Elmhurst Stores Ltd and are processing receipts and payments.

The amount shown below has been received from customers and the transaction is ready to be entered into the cash book module of your digital bookkeeping system.

Receipt 451
15 June 20-8
Cash sales from customers:
Total £4,517.40 including VAT

(a)   Make the necessary entries in the cash book by:

- selecting the correct side of the cash book

- choosing the description for the details column of the cash book

- making the entry in the cash book

Cash book	✔
Cash book – receipts	
Cash book – payments	

Description for details column	✔
Total	
VAT	
Trade receivables	
Sales	

(b) Identify which document you will refer to for details of payments to be recorded in the cash book.

Information required	Document
Details of amounts banked	
Details of recurring payments made through the bank account	

Select your document from the following list: Cash sales receipts, Internet banking payments schedule, Paying-in slip counterfoils, Sales invoices, Standing order and direct debit schedule.

9.12 You are the cashier at Star Ltd. Today, 1 July 20-7, you are setting up a recurring payment in the digital bookkeeping system.

Standing order and direct debit schedule:

> Star Ltd has signed a contract for a year to pay £162, including VAT, each month from Galaxy Ltd for providing digital bookkeeping services. Date of first payment: 1 July 20-7.

Show the necessary entries by:

- selecting the correct side of the cash book
- recording the entry in the standing order and direct debit schedule
- recording the entry in the cash book

Cash book	✔
Cash book – receipts	
Cash book – payments	

Date 20-7	Details	Total £	VAT £	Net £	Frequency	Recurrences

Date 20-7	Details	Total £	VAT £	Net £

10 Petty cash book

10.1 The imprest system for petty cash means that:

(a)	Petty cash payments up to a stated amount can be authorised by the petty cashier	
(b)	Petty cash vouchers must have relevant documentation attached	
(c)	The petty cash float is restored to the same amount for the beginning of each week or month	
(d)	Petty cash vouchers are numbered and the number is recorded in the petty cash book	

10.2 A petty cash account has a balance b/d of £150 at the beginning of a month. During the month, payments are made from petty cash which total £108. Which **one** of the following transactions will restore the balance of petty cash account to £150?

(a)	Debit bank £150; credit petty cash £150	
(b)	Debit petty cash £108; credit bank £108	
(c)	Debit petty cash £42; credit bank £42	
(d)	Debit bank £108; credit petty cash £108	

10.3 Show whether the following statements are true or false.

Statement		True	False
(a)	Payments are recorded on the debit side of petty cash book		
(b)	A petty cash book may combine the roles of a book of prime entry and double-entry bookkeeping		
(c)	Petty cash vouchers are authorised for payment by the petty cashier or a manager		
(d)	The totals of the petty cash analysis columns are transferred to general ledger where they are debited to the appropriate expense account		

10.4   A firm's petty cash book is operated on the imprest system. The imprest amount is £250. At the end of a particular period, the analysis columns are totalled as follows: VAT £13.42; postage £29.18; travel £45.47; stationery £33.29; cleaning £18.54.

How much cash will be required to restore the imprest amount for the next period?

(a)	£250.00	
(b)	£126.48	
(c)	£139.90	
(d)	£110.10	

10.5   A firm's petty cash book is operated on the imprest system. The imprest amount is £125. At the end of a particular period, the petty cash remaining comprised:

2 x £10 notes, 5 x £5 notes, 4 x £1 coins, 3 x 50p coins, 6 x 20p coins, 3 x 10p coins, 3 x 5p coins, 8 x 1p coins.

Provided no errors or discrepancies have occurred, what is the amount of payments that will be recorded in the petty cash book for the period?

(a)	£72.77	
(b)	£52.23	
(c)	£72.65	
(d)	£125.00	

10.6   The petty cashier of the business where you work tops up the petty cash at the end of the month with £110 withdrawn from the bank.

What will be the entries in the general ledger?

Select your account names from the following list: Bank, Cash, Petty cash book, Purchases, Payables ledger control, Sales, Receivables ledger control, Value Added Tax.

General ledger

Account name	Amount £	Debit	Credit

10.7 Wyvern Property maintains a petty cash book as both a book of prime entry and part of the double-entry accounting system. The following transactions all took place on 30 June and have been recorded in the petty cash book as shown below. No entries have yet been made in the general ledger.

Petty cash book

Date	Details	Amount	Date	Details	Amount	VAT	Postages	Travel expenses	Stationery
20-4		£	20-4		£	£	£	£	£
30 Jun	Balance b/f	68.00	30 Jun	Taxi	14.88	2.48		12.40	
30 Jun	Bank	57.00	30 Jun	Copy paper	18.72	3.12			15.60
			30 Jun	Post office	11.50		11.50		
			30 Jun	Rail fare	22.35			22.35	
				Balance c/d	57.55				
		125.00			125.00	5.60	11.50	34.75	15.60

What will be the entries in the general ledger?

Select your account names from the following list: Balance b/f, Balance c/d, Bank, Copy paper, Petty cash book, Postages, Post office, Rail fare, Stationery, Taxi, Travel expenses, Value Added Tax.

General ledger

Account name	Amount	Debit	Credit
	£		

10.8 The following petty cash book shows a number of transactions of Elliotts Limited for July 20-6. The petty cash book is kept solely as a book of prime entry.

Petty Cash Book											**PCB35**
Date	Details	Amount	Date	Details	Amount	VAT	Travel	Postages	Stationery	Payables ledger
		£			£	£	£	£	£	£
1 Jul	Balance b/f	200.00								
			6 Jul	Post office	11.55			11.55		
			9 Jul	Rail fare	17.60		17.60			
			11 Jul	Envelopes	9.60	1.60			8.00	
			12 Jul	Post office	10.00			10.00		
14 Jul	T Irwin (postage)	6.25								
			19 Jul	Taxi	10.08	1.68	8.40			
			22 Jul	J Clarke (PL)	18.25					18.25
			25 Jul	Marker pens	6.24	1.04			5.20	
					83.32	4.32	26.00	21.55	13.20	18.25
31 Jul	Bank	77.07								
			31 Jul	Balance c/d	200.00					
		283.32			283.32					
1 Aug	Balance b/d	200.00								

(a) **You are to** transfer the data from the petty cash book into the general ledger accounts (including cash book) as at 31 July 20-6. Note that a petty cash account is required.

(b) Show the entry that will be recorded in payables ledger as at 31 July 20-6.

10.9 This is a summary of petty cash payments made by Dalbeith & Co:

Post office paid	£10.70 (no VAT)
City Taxis paid	£14.40 including VAT at 20%
Repair Shop Ltd paid	£18.80 plus VAT at 20%

(a) Record the above transactions, in the order in which they are shown, in the petty cash book below.

(b) Total the petty cash book and show the balance carried down.

Select your entries for the Details columns from the following list: Amount, Balance b/f, Balance c/d, City Taxis, Details, Postages, Post office, Repairs, Repair Shop Ltd, Travel, VAT.

Petty cash book

Debit side		Credit side					
Details	Amount £	Details	Amount £	VAT £	Postages £	Travel £	Repairs £
Balance b/f	150.00						

10.10 Part way through the month, the petty cash account of a business had a balance of £93.30. The cash in the petty cash box was checked and the following notes and coins were present.

Notes and coins	£
4 x £10 notes	40.00
7 x £5 notes	35.00
9 x £1 coins	9.00
13 x 50p coins	6.50
10 x 10p coins	1.00
17 x 5p coins	0.85

(a)   Reconcile the cash amount in the petty cash box with the balance on the petty cash account.

Amount in petty cash box	£
Balance on petty cash account	£
Difference	£

At the end of the month, the cash in the petty cash box was £45.65.

(b)   Complete the petty cash reimbursement below to restore the imprest amount of £175.

Petty cash reimbursement	
Date	30 Apr 20-5
Amount required to restore the cash in the petty cash box	£

10.11 You are the bookkeeper at Haynes Ltd and you are dealing with the analysed petty cash book.

Today is 31 August 20-2 and there is one last petty cash payment for the month to be recorded: an amount of £17.46 including VAT has been paid for stationery.

(a) Calculate the VAT and net amounts to be recorded in the petty cash book.

VAT £	Net £

Before the petty cash payment in (a) was recorded, the stationery analysis column totalled £54.39.

(b) Calculate the total of the stationery analysis column after the payment in (a) is recorded.

£ _____

After all the August petty cash payments have been recorded, an amount of £21.33 was left in the petty cash float. On 31 August the petty cash float was topped up to the imprest amount of £250.

(c) What will be the entry in the petty cash book to record this transaction?

Details	Amount £	Debit ✔	Credit ✔

Select your details from the following list: Bank, Cash receipt, Cash sales, Credit sales, Trade payables, Trade receivables.

11 The trial balance

11.1 This task is about totalling and balancing ledger accounts.

The following account is in the general ledger at the close of day on 31 May 20-6:

Bank loan

20-6	Details	Amount £	20-6	Details	Amount £
31 May	Bank	750	1 May	Balance b/f	8,250
			10 May	Bank	2,200

- What is the balance brought down at 1 June on the account?

- Indicate whether the balance brought down is debit or credit.

Account name	Balance £	Debit ✔	Credit ✔
Bank loan			

11.2 Indicate which of the statements about the trial balance are true or false?

Statement	True	False
A trial balance is a regular arithmetic check of the accuracy of the bookkeeping		
Any errors made by the bookkeeper will be shown by the trial balance		
Credit balances shown on the trial balance represent assets and expenses		
Balances from the trial balance form the basis for the production of financial statements		

11.3   Indicate whether the following accounts will have a debit balance or a credit balance:

Account name	Debit	Credit
Bank (overdraft)		
Purchases		
Sales returns		
Payables ledger control		
Vehicles		
Discounts allowed		
Rent received		
Capital		

11.4 From the account balances below, prepare the trial balance of Vipin Das as at 30 April 20-1 (use the trial balance layout provided).

	£
Petty cash	120
Sales	45,500
Bank (cash at bank)	13,600
Office equipment	4,200
Capital	20,000
Purchases	32,800
Payables ledger control	14,300
Receivables ledger control	20,900
Purchases returns	190
Discounts allowed	230
Rent paid	10,400
Value Added Tax (owing to HMRC)	2,260

Trial balance of Vipin Das as at 30 April 20-1

Account name	Debit £	Credit £
Petty cash		
Sales		
Bank (cash at bank)		
Office equipment		
Capital		
Purchases		
Payables ledger control		
Receivables ledger control		
Purchases returns		
Discounts allowed		
Rent paid		
Value Added Tax (owing to HMRC)		
TOTALS		

11.5 From the account balances below, prepare the trial balance of Elmhurst Enterprises as at 31 May 20-1 (use the trial balance layout provided). The bookkeeper has omitted to open a capital account.

	£
Bank (cash at bank)	11,420
Purchases	69,300
Wages	15,800
Sales	105,400
Sales returns	280
Receivables ledger control	17,600
Rent paid	5,750
Drawings	5,000
Office equipment	3,900
General expenses	4,600
Payables ledger control	7,300
Value Added Tax (owing to HMRC)	3,100
Discounts allowed	350
Capital	?

Trial balance of Elmhurst Enterprises as at 31 May 20-1

Account name	Debit £	Credit £
Bank (cash at bank)		
Purchases		
Wages		
Sales		
Sales returns		
Receivables ledger control		
Rent paid		
Drawings		
Office equipment		
General expenses		
Payables ledger control		
Value Added Tax (owing to HMRC)		
Discounts received		
Capital		
TOTALS		

Answers to chapter activities

1 The accounting system

1.1   (a)   Cash sale

1.2   (c)   The first place an entry is recorded in the accounting records

1.3   (c)   Cash and credit and other financial transactions

1.4   (b)   Customers who buy goods and services on a credit basis

1.5   A **trial balance** sets out in two columns the balances of the **ledger accounts** of a business. The **totals** of the two columns should **agree**. The debit column includes the accounts of **receivables** and the credit column includes the accounts of **payables**. This provides the **managers** of a business with important and useful financial information.

1.6   (c)   Assets, liabilities, income and expenses

1.7   (b)   Income – Expenses = Profit

1.8   (b)   Assets – Liabilities = Capital

2 Financial documents for sales

2.1   (a)

INVOICE				**No** 1689		
PRAXIS STATIONERY				**Date** 09 07 20-3		
45 Jarvis Street						
Mereford MR1 2GH						
VAT Reg 831 8627 06						
To						
Dover Designs						
68 Whitecliff Street, Granstow, GR3 7GH				Customer code DO109		
				Delivery note no 246		

Quantity	Product code	Unit price (£)	Total (£)	Net (£)	VAT (£)	Total (£)
100	BX100	4.00	400.00	320.00	64.00	384.00

(b)   (c)   Request a credit note for the amount of the discount (including VAT)

2.2

STATEMENT OF ACCOUNT			**To** Rosetti Associates
PRAXIS STATIONERY			**Date** 31 08 20-3
45 Jarvis Street, Mereford MR1 2GH			

Date	Details	Amount £	Balance outstanding £
1 August	Invoice 1748	4,567.89	4,567.89
9 August	Invoice 1778	2,457.60	7,025.49
10 August	Invoice 1783	4,678.30	11,703.79
17 August	Credit note 319	280.50	11,423.29
29 August	Cheque	4,287.39	7,135.90

2.3

Product	Customer	General Ledger Code	Customer Code
Copy paper	Britmore Ltd	GL4002	BRI45
Gel pens	Coldring Limited	GL4003	COL12
Box files	Artex Limited	GL4018	ART09
Black printer ink	Coleman Trading	GL4017	COL10
Archive storage boxes	Bristol Wholesale	GL4008	BRI25
Suspension files	Britmore Limited	GL4018	BRI45

2.4 **(c)** A credit note

2.5 **(a)** (b) £128.00

  (b) (b) £768.00

2.6 **(a)**

Customer	£	Date
Wyre plc	*582.00	20 April 20-7
CDS Ltd	**1,123.20	24 April 20-7

*£500 - £15 PPD = £485 + £97 VAT = £582

** £960 - £24 PPD = £936 + £187.20 VAT = £1,123.20

  (b) (c) Receivables ledger

3

Double-entry and the accounting equation

3.1 (c) In the ledgers

3.2 (a) Payables ledger

3.3

	Debit	**Credit**
Money paid for **Purchases**	Purchases	Bank
Money received from **Sales**	Bank	Sales
Rent paid for premises used	Rent paid	Bank
Rent received for premises let	Bank	Rent received
Motor expenses paid	Motor expenses	Bank
Payment for **advertising** costs	Advertising	Bank
Stationery bill paid	Stationery	Bank
Loan received	Bank	Loan
Loan repayment made	Loan	Bank

3.4

Debit			**Sales Account**			**Credit**
Date	**Details**	**£**	**Date**	**Details**		**£**
			1 Feb	Bank		5,000
			2 Feb	Bank		7,500
			5 Feb	Bank		9,300

Debit			**Purchases Account**			**Credit**
Date	**Details**	**£**	**Date**	**Details**		**£**
1 Feb	Bank	3,500				
3 Feb	Bank	5,000				

Debit			Wages Account		Credit
Date	**Details**	**£**	**Date**	**Details**	**£**
2 Feb	Bank	2,510			

Debit			Rent Paid Account		Credit
Date	**Details**	**£**	**Date**	**Details**	**£**
4 Feb	Bank	780			

Debit			Bank Loan Account		Credit
Date	**Details**	**£**	**Date**	**Details**	**£**
			3 Feb	Bank	12,500

3.5 **(a)**

Statement		True	False
(a)	Liabilities equals capital plus assets		✔
(b)	Assets equals liabilities minus capital		✔
(c)	Capital equals assets minus liabilities	✔	

(b)

Item		Asset	Liability
(a)	Vehicles	✔	
(b)	Bank loan		✔
(c)	Money owing by trade receivables	✔	
(d)	Inventory	✔	
(e)	Cash	✔	
(f)	VAT owing to HM Revenue & Customs		✔

3.6

Assets	Liabilities	Capital
£	£	£
50,000	0	50,000
40,000	10,000	30,000
55,200	24,950	30,250
58,980	18,220	40,760
40,320	15,980	24,340
73,350	24,760	48,590

3.7

Transaction		Debit	Credit
(a)	Capital account increases		✔
(b)	Liability account increases		✔
(c)	Asset account decreases		✔
(d)	Liability account decreases	✔	
(e)	Asset account increases	✔	

3.8 (a) - (b) Vehicles have been bought for £10,000, paid from the bank

(b) - (c) Inventory has been bought for £6,000, paid from the bank

(c) - (d) Inventory has been bought for £3,000, on credit from a supplier

(d) - (e) Further vehicle bought for £8,000, paid for with £3,000 from the bank and a loan for £5,000

(e) - (f) Owner introduces £10,000 additional capital, paid into the bank

3.9

Dr			Bank			Cr
20-4	Details	£	20-4	Details	£
4 March	Capital	5,000	11 March	Purchases	375
5 March	Bank loan	15,000	15 March	Rent	400
7 March	Sales	670	16 March	Purchases	1,380
18 March	Sales	430	22 March	Telephone	180
26 March	Sales	1,320	29 March	Insurance	1,200

Account	Date	Dr or Cr	Details	Amount £
Capital	4 March	Cr	Bank	5,000
Bank loan	5 March	Cr	Bank	15,000
Sales	7 March	Cr	Bank	670
Purchases	11 March	Dr	Bank	375
Rent	15 March	Dr	Bank	400
Purchases	16 March	Dr	Bank	1,380
Sales	18 March	Cr	Bank	430
Telephone	22 March	Dr	Bank	180
Sales	26 March	Cr	Bank	1,320
Insurance	29 March	Dr	Bank	1,200

3.10

(a)

Dr			Egret Building (Receivables Ledger)			Cr
20-4	**Details**	**£**	**20-4**	**Details**		**£**
24 Aug	Sales	900.00	25 Aug	Sales returns		160.00
27 Aug	Sales	140.00	31 Aug	Balance c/d		1,240.00
28 Aug	Sales	360.00				
		1,400.00				1,400.00
1 Sep	Balance b/d	1,240.00				

(b)

Dr			Curtis & Curtis (Payables Ledger)			Cr
20-4	**Details**	**£**	**20-4**	**Details**		**£**
31 Aug	Balance c/d	1,013.50	24 Aug	Purchases		496.00
			26 Aug	Purchases		157.50
			31 Aug	Purchases		360.00
		1,013.50				1,013.50
			1 Sep	Balance b/d		1,013.50

(c)

Dr						
		R & T Engineering (Payables Ledger)				Cr
20-4	**Details**	**£**	**20-4**	**Details**		**£**
24 Aug	Purchases returns	160.00	25 Aug	Purchases		240.00
31 Aug	Balance c/d	1,140.00	28 Aug	Purchases		720.00
			31 Aug	Purchases		340.00
		1,300.00				1,300.00
			1 Sep	Balance b/d		1,140.00

(d)

Dr						
		Motor expenses (General Ledger)				Cr
20-4	**Details**	**£**	**20-4**	**Details**		**£**
5 Aug	Bank	150.40	31 Aug	Balance c/d		728.60
7 Aug	Bank	382.00				
9 Aug	Bank	69.30				
16 Aug	Bank	126.90				
		728.60				728.60
1 Sep	Balance b/d	728.60				

4

Accounting for sales, returns and discounts

4.1 (b) Credit note

4.2 (d) Credit note issued; sales returns day book; sales returns account; VAT account; receivables ledger control account; customer's account

4.3 (d) Invoice

4.4 (a)

				Sales Day Book		SDB65
Date	**Customer name**	**Invoice number**	**Account code**	**Total**	**VAT**	**Net**
20-4				£	£	£
3 Nov	Dines Stores	3592	RL086	318.00	53.00	265.00
5 Nov	Raven Retailers Ltd	3593	RL170	402.00	67.00	335.00
6 Nov	Meadow Golf Club	3594	RL135	210.00	35.00	175.00
10 Nov	Wyvern Stores	3595	RL195	546.00	91.00	455.00
11 Nov	Dines Stores	3596	RL086	348.00	58.00	290.00
13 Nov	Teme Sports Ltd	3597	RL178	378.00	63.00	315.00
17 Nov	Raven Retailers Ltd	3598	RL170	1,344.00	224.00	1,120.00
19 Nov	Teme Sports Ltd	3599	RL178	990.00	165.00	825.00
21 Nov	Dines Stores	3600	RL086	424.80	70.80	354.00
24 Nov	Meadow Golf Club	3601	RL135	297.60	49.60	248.00
27 Nov	Wyvern Stores	3602	RL195	627.60	104.60	523.00
30 Nov	Totals for month			5,886.00	981.00	4,905.00
				GL1200	GL2200	GL4100

(b)

GENERAL LEDGER

Dr	Receivables Ledger Control Account (GL1200)			Cr
20-4		£	20-4	£
30 Nov	Sales Day Book SDB65	5,886.00		

Dr	Value Added Tax Account (GL2200)			Cr
20-4		£	20-4	£
			30 Nov Sales Day Book SDB65	981.00

Dr	Sales Account (GL4100)			Cr
20-4		£	20-4	£
			30 Nov Sales Day Book SDB65	4,905.00

RECEIVABLES LEDGER

Dr	Dines Stores (RL086)				Cr
20-4			£	20-4	£
3 Nov	Sales	SDB65	318.00		
11 Nov	Sales	SDB65	348.00		
21 Nov	Sales	SDB65	424.80		

Dr	Meadow Golf Club (RL135)				Cr
20-4			£	20-4	£
6 Nov	Sales	SDB65	210.00		
24 Nov	Sales	SDB65	297.60		

Dr	Raven Retailers Limited (RL170)				Cr
20-4			£	20-4	£
5 Nov	Sales	SDB65	402.00		
17 Nov	Sales	SDB65	1,344.00		

Dr	Teme Sports Limited (RL178)				Cr
20-4			£	20-4	£
13 Nov	Sales	SDB65	378.00		
19 Nov	Sales	SDB65	990.00		

Dr	Wyvern Stores (RL195)				Cr
20-4			£	20-4	£
10 Nov	Sales	SDB65	546.00		
27 Nov	Sales	SDB65	627.60		

4.5 **(a)**

Sales Returns Day Book						SRDB22
Date	Customer name	Credit note number	Account code	Total	VAT	Net
20-4				£	£	£
10 Nov	Dines Stores	831	RL086	66.00	11.00	55.00
14 Nov	Wyvern Stores	832	RL195	72.00	12.00	60.00
19 Nov	Meadow Golf Club	833	RL135	55.20	9.20	46.00
24 Nov	Teme Sports Ltd	834	RL178	152.40	25.40	127.00
28 Nov	Dines Stores	835	RL086	104.40	17.40	87.00
30 Nov	Totals for month			450.00	75.00	375.00
				GL1200	GL2200	GL4110

(b)

GENERAL LEDGER

Dr		Receivables Ledger Control Account (GL1200)				Cr
20-4			£	20-4		£
30 Nov	Sales Day Book SDB65	5,886.00		30 Nov	Sales Returns Day Book SRDB22	450.00

Dr		Value Added Tax Account (GL2200)				Cr
20-4			£	20-4		£
30 Nov	Sales Returns Day Book SRDB22	75.00		30 Nov	Sales Day Book SDB65	981.00

Dr		Sales Returns Account (GL4110)			Cr
20-4			£	20-4	£
30 Nov	Sales Returns Day Book SRDB22	375.00			

RECEIVABLES LEDGER

Dr				Dines Stores (RL086)			Cr
20-4			£	20-4			£
3 Nov	Sales	SDB65	318.00	10 Nov	Sales Returns SRDB22		66.00
11 Nov	Sales	SDB65	348.00	28 Nov	Sales Returns SRDB22		104.40
21 Nov	Sales	SDB65	424.80				

Dr				Meadow Golf Club (RL135)			Cr
20-4			£	20-4			£
6 Nov	Sales	SDB65	210.00	19 Nov	Sales Returns SRDB22		55.20
24 Nov	Sales	SDB65	297.60				

Dr				Teme Sports Limited (RL178)			Cr
20-4			£	20-4			£
13 Nov	Sales	SDB65	378.00	24 Nov	Sales Returns SRDB22		152.40
19 Nov	Sales	SDB65	990.00				

Dr				Wyvern Stores (RL195)			Cr
20-4			£	20-4			£
10 Nov	Sales	SDB65	546.00	14 Nov	Sales Returns SRDB22		72.00
27 Nov	Sales	SDB65	627.60				

4.6   (a) and (b)

Sales day book

Date 20-4	Customer name	Invoice number	Total £	VAT £	Net £	Sales type 1 £	Sales type 2 £
30 June	Olander Ltd	1895	1,920	320	1,600	1,600	
30 June	Boltz & Co	1896	5,040	840	4,200		4,200
30 June	Ravells	1897	576	96	480	480	
	Totals		7,536	1,256	6,280	2,080	4,200

4.7 **(a)** **Receivables ledger**

Account name	Amount £	Debit	Credit
Upton Ltd	2,016	✔	
Bromyards	3,408	✔	
Kempsey & Co	4,272	✔	
Fernhill plc	2,448	✔	

General ledger

Account name	Amount £	Debit	Credit
Sales	10,120		✔
Value Added Tax	2,024		✔
Receivables ledger control	12,144	✔	

(b) **Receivables ledger**

Account name	Amount £	Debit	Credit
Drake & Co	336		✔
Hanbury Trading	1,008		✔

General ledger

Account name	Amount £	Debit	Credit
Sales returns	1,120	✔	
Value Added Tax	224	✔	
Receivables ledger control	1,344		✔

(c) **Receivables ledger**

Account name	Amount £	Debit	Credit
Powick & Co	30		✔
Heath Trading	42		✔

General ledger

Account name	Amount £	Debit	Credit
Discounts allowed	60	✔	
Value Added Tax	12	✔	
Receivables ledger control	72		✔

4.8   (a)   **General ledger**

Account name	Amount £	Debit	Credit
Discounts allowed	120	✔	
VAT	24	✔	
Receivables ledger control	144		✔

(b)   **Receivables ledger**

Account name	Amount £	Debit	Credit
Khan Ltd	66		✔

4.9

Sales day book

Date 20-4	Customer name	Invoice number	Total £	VAT £	Net £	Product S12 £	Product T12 £
30 June	Hawke Ltd	2132	360.00	60.00	300.00		300.00
30 June	T Martin	2133	450.00	75.00	375.00	375.00	
30 June	S Garner	2134	630.00	105.00	525.00	525.00	
30 June	JEC Ltd	2135	180.00	30.00	150.00		150.00
	Totals		1,620.00	270.00	1,350.00	900.00	450.00

4.10   (a)

Daybook	✔
Sales day book	✔
Sales returns day book	
Purchases day book	
Discounts allowed day book	

Date 20-3	Name	Invoice number	Total £	VAT £	Net £
10 Jun	Locksafe & Co	35146	480.00	80.00	400.00

(b)

Purchases: security locks	
Sales: security alarms	
Sales: security locks	✔
Sales returns: security locks	

(c)

As a debit entry	
As a credit entry	✔

4.11

20-9	Details	Amount £	20-9	Details	Amount £
1 May	Balance b/f	1,834	15 May	Sales Returns	154
12 May	Sales	962	18 May	Bank	1,207
			31 May	Balance c/d	1,435
	Total	2,796		Total	2,796
1 Jun	Balance b/d	1,435			

4.12 (a)

Account name	Amount £	Debit ✔	Credit ✔
Sales Returns	420.00	✔	
VAT	84.00	✔	
Receivables ledger control	504.00		✔

(b)

Account name	Amount £	Debit ✔	Credit ✔
Bingham Ltd	30.00		✔

5 Process receipts from customers

5.1 (a) Sales documention reference numbers

5.2 (c) Same amount in words and figures, in date, signature of customer

5.3 (a) Invoice 392 is for £690 and not for £590

(b) Credit note 295 for £90 has not been allowed for on the remittance advice

5.4 (a)

20-6	Details	£	Discrepancies
4 May	Invoice 5207	2,385	Incorrect invoice number
10 May	Credit note 84	−65	Incorrectly recorded
12 May	Invoice 5314	1,459	Incorrect date
22 May	Credit note 91	−112	Incorrect amount
29 May	Invoice 5465	2,671	No discrepancy

(b) (d) £30 overpaid

(c) *£5,101.20

* £5,232 x 5/6 = £4,360 net of VAT
£4,360 − £109 PPD = £4,251 + £850.20 VAT = £5,101.20

(d)

Date 20-6	Detail	£	Outstanding amount £
1 May	Opening balance	2,450	1,000
14 May	Invoice 5332	1,576	438
26 May	Credit note 102	−338	0

6 Financial documents for purchases

6.1 (b) Delivery note

6.2 (c) The payables ledger

6.3 (a) Purchases

6.4

(a) Who has supplied the chairs?

Helicon Furniture

(b) What is the problem with the consignment?

2 chairs damaged

(c) What document would be issued by the supplier to adjust the account of Praxis Stationery?

Credit note

(d) Where in the supplier's accounting records would the account of Praxis Stationery be maintained?

Receivables ledger

6.5 Has the correct purchase price of the chairs been charged? Yes or No?   YES

Has the correct discount been applied? Yes or No?   NO

What would be the VAT amount charged if the invoice was correct?   £288.00

What would be the total amount charged if the invoice was correct?   £1,728.00

6.6 Has the correct number of tables been supplied? Yes or No?   NO

Has the correct type of table been supplied? Yes or No?   YES

What will be the total of the invoice on the basis of the details on the   £384.00
delivery note?

If a credit note were issued, what would be the total, including VAT?   £76.80

6.7

Purpose	Document
Information from the supplier regarding the goods or services required	Price enquiry
Issued to the supplier stating the goods or services requested	Purchase order
Used by the buyer to record receipt of goods	Goods received note
Sent to the supplier with faulty goods	Goods returns note

6.8

Discrepancy	
Buyer details	✔
Quantity of goods	✔
Date of credit note	✔
Net amount	
VAT amount	
Total amount	

7 Accounting for purchases, returns and discounts

7.1 (a) Purchases invoice

7.2 (c) Invoice received; purchases day book; purchases account; VAT account; payables ledger control account; supplier's account

7.3 (c) Debit purchases; debit VAT; credit payables ledger control

7.4 (a)

Purchases Day Book				Total	VAT	PDB55 Net
Date	Supplier name	Invoice number	Account code	Total	VAT	Net
20-2				£	£	£
3 May	Malvern Manufacturing	7321	PL625	204.00	34.00	170.00
9 May	S Burston	SB745	PL530	318.00	53.00	265.00
12 May	Iley Supplies Ltd	4721	PL605	540.00	90.00	450.00
18 May	SG Enterprises	3947	PL720	990.00	165.00	825.00
23 May	S Burston	SB773	PL530	512.40	85.40	427.00
30 May	Malvern Manufacturing	7408	PL625	436.80	72.80	364.00
31 May	Totals for month			3,001.20	500.20	2,501.00
				GL2350	GL2200	GL5100

(b)   **GENERAL LEDGER**

Dr	**Value Added Tax Account** (GL2200)		Cr
20-2	£	20-2	£
31 May Purchases Day Book PDB55	500.20		

Dr	**Payables Ledger Control Account** (GL2350)		Cr
20-2	£	20-2	£
		31 May Purchases Day Book PDB55	3,001.20

Dr			**Purchases Account** (GL5100)			Cr
20-2		£	20-2			£
31 May	Purchases Day Book					
	PDB55	2,501.00				

PAYABLES LEDGER

Dr		£	**S Burston** (PL530)			Cr
20-2		£	20-2			£
			9 May	Purchases	PDB55	318.00
			23 May	Purchases	PDB55	512.40

Dr		£	**Iley Supplies Limited** (PL605)			Cr
20-2		£	20-2			£
			12 May	Purchases		540.00

Dr		£	**Malvern Manufacturing** (PL625)			Cr
20-2		£	20-2			£
			3 May	Purchases	PDB55	204.00
			30 May	Purchases	PDB55	436.80

Dr		£	**SG Enterprises** (PL720)			Cr
20-2		£	20-2			£
			18 May	Purchases	PDB55	990.00

7.5   **(a)**

Purchases Returns Day Book						PRDB14
Date	Supplier name	Credit note number	Account code	Total	VAT	Net
20-2				£	£	£
11 May	Malvern Manufacturing	CN345	PL625	84.00	14.00	70.00
17 May	Iley Supplies Ltd	CN241	PL605	102.00	17.00	85.00
24 May	SG Enterprises	85	PL720	30.00	5.00	25.00
31 May	S Burston	SB95	PL530	66.00	11.00	55.00
31 May	Totals for month			282.00	47.00	235.00
				GL2350	GL2200	GL5110

(b)   **GENERAL LEDGER**

Dr		**Value Added Tax Account** (GL2200)			Cr
20-2		£	20-2		£
31 May	Purchases Day Book PDB55	500.20	31 May	Purchases Returns Day Book PRDB14	47.00

Dr		**Payables Ledger Control Account** (GL2350)			Cr
20-2		£	20-2		£
31 May	Purchases Returns Day Book PRDB14	282.00	31 May	Purchases Day Book PDB55	3,001.20

Dr		**Purchases Returns Account** (GL5110)			Cr
20-2		£	20-2		£
			31 May	Purchases Returns Day Book PRDB14	235.00

PAYABLES LEDGER

Dr		**S Burston** (PL530)				Cr
20-2		£	20-2			£
31 May	Purchases Returns PRDB14	66.00	9 May	Purchases	PDB55	318.00
			23 May	Purchases	PDB55	512.40

Dr			Iley Supplies Limited (PL605)			Cr
20-2		£	20-2			£
17 May	Purchases Returns		12 May	Purchases	PDB55	540.00
	PRDB14	102.00				

Dr			Malvern Manufacturing (PL625)			Cr
20-2		£	20-2			£
11 May	Purchases Returns		3 May	Purchases	PDB55	204.00
	PRDB14	84.00	30 May	Purchases	PDB55	436.80

Dr			SG Enterprises (PL720)			Cr
20-2		£	20-2			£
24 May	Purchases Returns		18 May	Purchases	PDB55	990.00
	PRDB14	30.00				

7.6 Purchases day book

Date 20-4	Supplier name	Invoice number	Total £	VAT £	Net £	Purchases type 1 £	Purchases type 2 £
30 June	King & Co	K641	2,016	336	1,680		1,680
30 June	Rossingtons	2129	3,072	512	2,560	2,560	
30 June	Moniz Ltd	M/149	2,208	368	1,840		1,840
	Totals		7,296	1,216	6,080	2,560	3,520

7.7 **(a)** **Payables ledger**

Account name	Amount £	Debit	Credit
H & L Ltd	6,528		✔
Sperrin & Co	2,208		✔
Hickmores	4,608		✔
Marklew plc	1,104		✔

General ledger

Account name	Amount £	Debit	Credit
Purchases	12,040	✔	
Value Added Tax	2,408	✔	
Payables ledger control	14,448		✔

(b) **Payables ledger**

Account name	Amount £	Debit	Credit
Marcer Transport	624	✔	
Schuller Ltd	432	✔	

General ledger

Account name	Amount £	Debit	Credit
Purchases returns	880		✔
Value Added Tax	176		✔
Payables ledger control	1,056	✔	

(c) **Payables ledger**

Account name	Amount £	Debit	Credit
DDE & Co	18	✔	
Transpo Ltd	24	✔	

General ledger

Account name	Amount £	Debit	Credit
Discounts received	35		✔
Value Added Tax	7		✔
Payables ledger control	42	✔	

7.8　(a)　**General ledger**

Account name	Amount £	Debit	Credit
Discounts received	195		✔
VAT	39		✔
Payables ledger control	234	✔	

(b)　**Payables ledger**

Account name	Amount £	Debit	Credit
Hussain plc	102	✔	

7.9

Purchases day book

Date 20-4	Supplier name	Invoice number	Total £	VAT £	Net £	Product S12 £	Product T12 £
30 June	Lyster Ltd	4681	1,200.00	200.00	1000.00	1,000.00	
30 June	T England	6234	432.00	72.00	360.00		360.00
30 June	Mere Ltd	1634	1,080.00	180.00	900.00		900.00
30 June	J Mehta	8561	480.00	80.00	400.00	400.00	
	Totals		3,192.00	532.00	2,660.00	1,400.00	1,260.00

7.10　(a)

Daybook	✔
Sales day book	
Purchases returns day book	
Purchases day book	✔
Discounts received day book	

Date 20-7	Name	Invoice number	Total £	VAT £	Net £
2 May	Linen Traders	3690	542.62	90.44	452.18
10 May	GoodFood Ltd	74/GF	718.04	119.67	598.37
15 May	PPE Supplies	45417	374.70	62.45	312.25
23 May	Fruit 'n Veg Ltd	1974	475.32	79.22	396.10
29 May	PPE Supplies	45761	223.20	37.20	186.00
	TOTALS		2,333.88	388.98	1,944.90

(b)

	✔
As a debit entry to receivables ledger control account	
As a debit entry to payables ledger control account	
As a credit entry to receivables ledger control account	
As a credit entry to payables ledger control account	✔

(c)

	✔
As a debit entry	✔
As a credit entry	

7.11 (a)

Account name	Amount £	Debit ✔	Credit ✔
Purchases	6,120.00	✔	
VAT	1,224.00	✔	
Payables ledger control	7,344.00		✔

(b)

Account name	Amount £	Debit ✔	Credit ✔
Carlton Ltd	24.00	✔	

7.12

20-6	Details	Amount £	20-6	Details	Amount £
5 June	Purchases Returns	174	1 June	Balance b/f	3,054
25 June	Bank	2,562	20 June	Purchases	1,526
30 June	Balance c/d	1,844			
	Total	4,580		Total	4,580
			1 July	Balance b/d	1,844

8 Process payments to suppliers

8.1 (a) An increase in the total amount owing shown on the statement of account

8.2 (c) Purchase invoices, purchase credit notes, total amount owing

8.3 (b) Will reduce the total amount shown as owing on the statement of account

8.4 (a) Payment for £1,000

(b) Invoice 790

(c) £360

8.5 (a) (b) Without a cheque to A Strauss & Co

(b) (c) 30 April

(c) (b) Invoice 2461, invoice 2479, credit note CN105

(d) (c) £3,640

8.6 (a)

Killeen & Co				
Park Road, Patchling, PG1 2DP				
STATEMENT OF ACCOUNT: Pierson Ltd				
Date 20-8	**Document number**	**Details**	**Amount £**	**✔**
3 June	CN 62	Goods returned	−125	
15 June	5205	Goods	2,109	
17 June	5232	Goods	1,095	
20 June	5302	Goods	1,746	✔
26 June	5417	Goods	822	
29 June	CN 75	Goods returned	−268	✔
30 June	5519	Goods	2,312	✔

(b)

Pierson Ltd BACS Remittance Advice To: Killeen & Co			
Date	Your reference		Amount £
3 June	CN 62		−125
15 June	5205		2,109
17 June	5232		1,095
26 June	5417		822
		TOTAL	3,901

8.7

20-4	Details	£	Discrepancies
2 April	Invoice 6318	1,890	Incorrect amount
5 April	Credit note 422	−75	Incorrect date
16 April	Invoice 6765	2,230	Incorrect invoice number
22 April	Credit note 438	−212	Not on statement
25 April	Invoice 6821	1,435	No discrepancy

9 Cash book

9.1 (c) BACS transfer from a trade receivable for £1,950

9.2 (a) **Receivables ledger**

Account name	Amount £	Debit	Credit
Delta & Co	325		✔
Boscawen Ltd	1,540		✔

(b) **General ledger**

Account name	Amount £	Debit	Credit
Receivables ledger control	325		✔
Receivables ledger control	1,540		✔

(c) **General ledger**

Account name	Amount £	Debit	Credit
Wages	1,265	✔	
Office equipment	1,968	✔	

9.3 **(a)** **Receivables ledger**

Account name	Amount £	Debit	Credit
Smithsons Ltd	2,325		✔
Egerton & Co	425		✔

(b) **General ledger**

Account name	Amount £	Debit	Credit
Receivables ledger control	*2,750		✔
Wages	1,175	✔	
Rent	1,200	✔	
Stationery	120	✔	

*£2,325 + £425

9.4 **(a)**   True

(b)   False – the balance b/d of £201 on 1 October shows that, according to the cash book, there is a bank overdraft.

(c)   **GENERAL LEDGER**

Dr			**Sales Account**			Cr
20-1			£	20-1		£
				30 Sep Cash	CB68	88

Dr			**Receivables Ledger Control Account**			Cr
20-1			£	20-1		£
				30 Sep Bank	CB68	1,580

Dr			**Payables Ledger Control Account**			Cr
20-1			£	20-1		£
30 Sep	Bank	CB68	1,940			

Dr			**Purchases Account**			Cr
20-1			£	20-1		£
30 Sep	Bank	CB68	192			

Dr			**General Expenses Account**			Cr
20-1			£	20-1		£
30 Sep	Cash	CB68	128			

Dr			**Wages Account**			Cr
20-1			£	20-1		£
30 Sep	Bank	CB68	1,254			

Dr			**Office Equipment Account**			Cr
20-1			£	20-1		£
30 Sep	Bank	CB68	1,440			

(d)

RECEIVABLES LEDGER

Dr				Albany Limited			Cr
20-1			£	20-1			£
				30 Sep	Bank	CB68	1,580

PAYABLES LEDGER

Dr				Nelson Stores			Cr
20-1			£	20-1			£
30 Sep	Bank	CB68	1,940				

9.5

Cash Book

Dr Date 20-7	Details	Cash £	Bank £	Cr Date 20-7	Details	Cash £	Bank £
3 Aug	Balance b/d	286		3 Aug	Balance b/d		3,472
4 Aug	Sales	334		3 Aug	Rent		760
5 Aug	Murphy Ltd		1,475	8 Aug	Rates		223
10 Aug	Balance c/d		3,870	8 Aug	JJ Supplies		490
				10 Aug	Drawings		400
				10 Aug	Wages	480	
				10 Aug	Balance c/d	140	
		620	5,345			620	5,345
11 Aug	Balance b/d	140		11 Aug	Balance b/d		3,870

Note: prompt payment discount for the transactions on 5 August and 8 August is not recorded in the cash book; instead, a credit note will be issued by the supplier to the customer (see Chapters 4 and 7).

9.6

Cash Book

Dr				Cr			
Date 20-3	Details	Cash £	Bank £	Date 20-3	Details	Cash £	Bank £
1 Mar	Balance b/d	200		1 Mar	Balance b/d		1,898
6 Mar	Court Ltd		1,236	2 Mar	Lindum Supplies		254
13 Mar	H Sweeney BACS		1,696	11 Mar	Rent		550
14 Mar	Sales	639		23 Mar	Wages	655	
24 Mar	Sales	786		26 Mar	Wyvern Council SO		195
28 Mar	Mills & Co Ltd BACS		477	27 Mar	Bank interest		45
				31 Mar	Balance c/d	970	467
		1,625	3,409			1,625	3,409
1 Apr	Balances b/d	970	467				

9.7 (c) Debit card payment to a trade payable for £940

9.8 **(a)**, **(c)** and **(d)** are true; **(b)** is false.

9.9 **(a)** **Cash book – credit side**

Details	Cash	Bank	VAT	Trade payables	Cash purchases	Stationery expenses
	£	£	£	£	£	£
Balance b/f						
Clark & Co	48		8		40	
T Kinnear	192		32		160	
Gaskin Ltd		1,690		1,690		
Bristow Stationery		144	24			120
Roussouw & Co		1,140		1,140		
Totals	240	2,974	64	2,830	200	120

(b) **Cash book – debit side**

Details	Cash	Bank	Trade receivables
	£	£	£
Balance b/f	642	1,022	
Passmores		455	455
S McNulty		833	833
Totals	642	2,310	1,288

(c) £402

(d) £664

(e) Credit

9.10 **(a)**

Cash book – credit side

Details	Cash	Bank	VAT	Trade payables	Cash purchases	Other expenses
	£	£	£	£	£	£
Balance b/f		2,417				
Mary Wallbank	192		32		160	
Wenton Council		425				425
Sanders plc		600		600		
J Panas		672		672		
Totals	192	4,114	32	1,272	160	425

(b)

Cash book – debit side

Details	Cash	Bank	Trade receivables	Other income
	£	£	£	£
Balance b/f	208			
LFJ plc		1,685	1,685	
Wragg Ltd		2,135	2,135	
Nikki Shah	200			200
Totals	408	3,820	3,820	200

(c) £216

(d) −£294

(e)

Account name	Amount	Debit	Credit
Wragg Ltd	2,135		✔

9.11 **(a)**

Cash book	✔
Cash book – receipts	✔
Cash book – payments	

Description for details column	✔
Total	
VAT	
Trade receivables	
Sales	✔

(b)

Information required	Document
Details of amounts banked	Paying-in slip counterfoils
Details of recurring payments made through the bank account	Standing order and direct debit schedule

9.12

Cash book	✔
Cash book – receipts	
Cash book – payments	✔

Date 20-7	Details	Total £	VAT £	Net £	Frequency	Recurrences
1 July	Galaxy Ltd	162	27	135	Monthly	12

Date 20-7	Details	Total £	VAT £	Net £
1 July	Galaxy Ltd	162	27	135

10 Petty cash book

10.1 (c) The petty cash float is restored to the same amount for the beginning of each week or month

10.2 (b) Debit petty cash £108; credit bank £108

10.3 (a) is false; the others are true

10.4 (c) £139.90

10.5 (a) £72.77

10.6 General ledger

Account name	Amount £	Debit	Credit
Petty cash book	110	✔	
Bank	110		✔

10.7 General ledger

Account name	Amount £	Debit	Credit
VAT	5.60	✔	
Postages	11.50	✔	
Travel expenses	34.75	✔	
Stationery	15.60	✔	
Bank	57.00		✔

10.8 **(a)**

GENERAL LEDGER

Dr	Value Added Tax Account			Cr
20-6		£	20-6	£
31 Jul	Petty cash book PCB35	4.32		

Dr	Travel Account			Cr
20-6		£	20-6	£
31 Jul	Petty cash book PCB35	26.00		

Dr	Postages Account			Cr
20-6		£	20-6	£
31 Jul	Petty cash book PCB35	21.55	14 Jul	Petty cash book PCB35	6.25

Dr	Stationery Account			Cr
20-6		£	20-6	£
31 Jul	Petty cash book PCB35	13.20		

Dr	Payables Ledger Control Account			Cr
20-6		£	20-6	£
31 Jul	Petty cash book PCB35	18.25		

Dr	Petty Cash Account				Cr
20-6		£	20-6		£
1 Jul	Balance b/d	200.00	31 Jul	Petty cash book PCB35	83.32
31 Jul	Petty cash book PCB35	6.25	31 Jul	Balance c/d	200.00
31 Jul	Bank CB	77.07			
		283.32			283.32
1 Aug	Balance b/d	200.00			

Dr	Cash Book				Cr
20-6		Bank	20-6		Bank
			31 Jul	Petty cash PCB35	77.07

(b)

PAYABLES LEDGER

Dr	J Clarke			Cr
20-6		£	20-6	£
22 Jul	Petty cash book PCB35	18.25		

10.9 (a) and (b)

Petty cash book

Debit side		Credit side					
Details	Amount	Details	Amount	VAT	Postages	Travel	Repairs
	£		£	£	£	£	£
Balance b/f	150.00	Post office	10.70		10.70		
		City Taxis	14.40	2.40		12.00	
		Repair Shop Ltd	22.56	3.76			18.80
		Balance c/d	102.34				
	150.00		150.00	6.16	10.70	12.00	18.80

10.10 (a)

Amount in petty cash box	£92.35
Balance on petty cash account	£93.30
Difference	£0.95

(b)

Petty cash reimbursement	
Date	30 Apr 20-5
Amount required to restore the cash in the petty cash box	£129.35

10.11 (a)

VAT	Net
£	£
2.91	14.55

(b) £68.94

(c)

Details	Amount	Debit	Credit
	£	✔	✔
Bank	228.67	✔	

11 The trial balance

11.1

Account name	Balance £	Debit ✔	Credit ✔
Bank loan	9,700		✔

11.2

Statement	True	False
A trial balance is a regular arithmetic check of the accuracy of the bookkeeping.	✔	
Any errors made by the bookkeeper will be shown by the trial balance.		✔
Credit balances shown on the trial balance represent assets and expenses.		✔
Balances from the trial balance form the basis for the production of financial statements.	✔	

11.3

Account name	Debit	Credit
Bank (overdraft)		✔
Purchases	✔	
Sales returns	✔	
Payables ledger control		✔
Vehicles	✔	
Discounts allowed	✔	
Rent received		✔
Capital		✔

11.4

Trial balance of Vipin Das as at 30 April 20-1

Account name	Debit £	Credit £
Petty cash	120	
Sales		45,500
Bank (cash at bank)	13,600	
Office equipment	4,200	
Capital		20,000
Purchases	32,800	
Payables ledger control		14,300
Receivables ledger control	20,900	
Purchases returns		190
Discounts allowed	230	
Rent paid	10,400	
Value Added Tax (owing to HMRC)		2,260
TOTALS	82,250	82,250

11.5

Trial balance of Elmhurst Enterprises as at 31 May 20-1

Account name	Debit £	Credit £
Bank (cash at bank)	11,420	
Purchases	69,300	
Wages	15,800	
Sales		105,400
Sales returns	280	
Receivables ledger control	17,600	
Rent paid	5,750	
Drawings	5,000	
Office equipment	3,900	
General expenses	4,600	
Payables ledger control		7,300
Value Added Tax (owing to HMRC)		3,100
Discounts received		350
Capital		17,500
TOTALS	133,650	133,650

Practice assessment 1

Assessment information

- This practice assessment contains **11 tasks** and you should attempt to complete **every** task.

- Each task is independent. You will not need to refer to your answers from previous tasks.

- Read every task carefully to make sure you understand what is required.

- Where the date is relevant, it is given in the task data.

- Both minus signs and brackets can be used to indicate negative numbers **unless** task instructions state otherwise.

- You must use a full stop to indicate a decimal point. For example, write 100.57, **not** 100,57 or 10057.

- You may use a comma to indicate a number in the thousands, but you don't have to. For example, 10000 and 10,000 are both acceptable.

- Mathematical rounding should be applied where appropriate.

Scenario

The tasks in this practice assessment are set in different business situations where the following apply:

- Businesses use a variety of bookkeeping systems.

- Double entry takes place in the general ledger.

- The VAT rate is 20%.

Task 1

This task is about manual and digital bookkeeping systems.

(a) Identify which document would be used for each of the purposes below.

Purpose	Document
Detailing a bank payment to a supplier	
Detailing bank receipts and payments for a given period, together with the bank balance or overdraft	
Detailing a low value payment made in cash for a business expense	
Detailing goods or services supplied by a seller to a buyer and indicating the amount owed and the required payment date	

For the documents, choose from the following options (use each once only):

Remittance advice
Petty cash voucher
Invoice
Bank statement

(b) The digital bookkeeping system that you use creates alphanumerical customer codes using the following format:

First four letters of customer name/two numerical digits

The current customer accounts in the receivables ledger are:

Customer name	Customer account code
Allinson & Co	ALLI01
Farias Flowers	FARI01
Nila Hair Salon	NILA01
Trade Supplies	TRAD01
Trader Tim Ltd	TRAD02
Ultimate Builders	ULTI01

Two new customer accounts shown below need to be coded.

Enter the relevant account codes for each that the digital bookkeeping system will create.

Customer name	Customer account code
Allied Stores	
Traditional Builders	

(c) Identify the book of prime entry being described in the statement below.

A day book detailing items returned to suppliers

	✔
Purchases day book	
Purchases returns day book	
Sales day book	
Sales returns day book	
Cash book	

(d) Identify whether each of the following statements regarding bookkeeping systems is true or false.

Statement	True ✔	False ✔
A manual bookkeeping system is always completely accurate		
A digital bookkeeping system enables electronic recording of purchases invoices, with automatic updating of accounts in the payables ledger		
A digital bookkeeping system allows reports, such as a trial balance, to be available on demand		

Task 2

This task is about principles of double-entry bookkeeping.

A business has the following assets and liabilities:

Assets and liabilities	£
Office equipment	2,105.00
Receivables	24,246.68
Payables	16,931.21
Bank (overdraft)	584.72
Vehicle	6,100.00
Value Added Tax (owing to HMRC)	1,211.34

(a) Show the accounting equation by inserting the appropriate figures.

Do not use minus signs or brackets.

Assets £	Liabilities £	Capital £

(b) The bank/cash entries have already taken place for the transactions which follow.

In the table below, show the dual effect of each transaction by identifying the appropriate effect for each. Select the effect from the options, each of which can be used more than once.

Transaction	Dual effect
Owner transfers a computer into the business	
A bank loan has been received to pay for new office equipment	
Settled a payable's account using the bank overdraft	
A receivable settles her account in cash	
Old office equipment sold for cash	

Options
Increase in asset and liability
Decrease in asset and liability
Increase in asset and capital
Increase and decrease of assets
Increase and decrease of liabilities

You are to create a new general ledger account in your digital bookkeeping system for the following transaction:

> *Rental income from tenant for office space*

Identify the ledger account that you create.

	✔
Rent paid	
Rent received	
Office expenses	
Sales	

Task 3

This task is about processing customer invoices or credit notes and entering in day books.

(a) Complete the following statement about trade discounts by identifying **one** of the options below.

A trade discount is offered to customers to ….

	✔
encourage them to pay early	
encourage business customers to buy regularly	

You are the bookkeeper at Car Parts Ltd and have prepared the following invoice today, 10 June 20-3.

Car Parts Ltd
Invoice no: 47124

To: Malvern Autos
Customer ref: MALV01
Date: 10 June 20-3

	£
20 litres Triple A engine oil at £6 per litre	120.00
VAT @ 20%	24.00
TOTAL	144.00

Payment by BACS preferred

(b)   **You are to** record the invoice in the digital bookkeeping system by:

- selecting the correct daybook

- making the necessary entries

Daybook	✔
Sales day book	
Sales returns day book	
Purchases day book	
Discounts allowed day book	

Date 20-3	Name	Account code	Invoice number	Total £	VAT £	Net £

(c)   Identify the general ledger account into which the net amount will be entered.

	✔
Purchases: engine oil	
Sales: car polish	
Sales: engine oil	
Sales: brake fluid	

(d)   Identify how the amount will be recorded in the general ledger account selected in (c).

	✔
As a debit entry	
As a credit entry	

Task 4

This task is about processing receipts from customers.

You are the bookkeeper at JA Trading. A receipt of £5,037 has been received from a credit customer, Blanca Limited. The following is an extract for Blanca Limited from your digital bookkeeping system, together with the remittance advice.

May sales list: Blanca Ltd		
Date **20-6**	**Details**	**Amount** **£**
3 May	Invoice 2471	1,659
10 May	Credit note 85	–210
21 May	Invoice 2523	1,345
25 May	Credit note 91	–47
30 May	Invoice 2547	2,106

Remittance Advice: Blanca Ltd
To: JA Trading
31 May 20-6

Date **20-6**	**Details**	**Amount** **£**
3 May	Invoice 2471	1,659
10 May	Credit note 85	–120
12 May	Invoice 2523	1,345
25 May	Credit note 91	47
30 May	Invoice 2457	2,106
TOTAL: Paid by BACS 31 May		5,037

(a) **You are to** identify the discrepancies (if any) between the transactions from the sales list and the transactions in the remittance advice.

20-4	**Details**	**£**	**Discrepancies**
3 May	Invoice 2471	1,659	
10 May	Credit note 85	–210	
21 May	Invoice 2523	1,345	
25 May	Credit note 91	–47	
30 May	Invoice 2547	2,106	

For the discrepancies column, choose from the following options (use each once only):

No discrepancy
Incorrect date
Incorrect invoice number
Incorrectly recorded
Incorrect amount

(b) What will be the balance of Blanca Limited's account after the payment of £5,037 has been allocated to its account?

	✔
£184 underpaid	
£184 overpaid	
£47 underpaid	
£47 overpaid	

(c) An invoice to supply goods for £2,470 plus VAT has been sent by JA Trading to Rooke Limited offering prompt payment discount of 3% for payment within seven days.

What will be the amount received by JA Trading if Rooke Limited pays within seven days?

£ [ ]

(d) The following remittance advice has been received by JA Trading from Stanton & Co:

Stanton & Co
BACS remittance advice

To: JA Trading
Date: 31 May 20-6
Amount: £2,545
Detail:
- £1,545 part payment of balance at 1 May 20-6
- £1,000 part payment of invoice 2495
- Full allocation of credit note 90 to invoice 2495

You are to show the outstanding amount for each entry after the remittance has been allocated.

Date 20-6	Detail	£	Outstanding amount £
1 May	Opening balance	2,545	
10 May	Invoice 2495	1,629	
25 May	Credit note 90	−186	

Task 5

This task is about processing supplier invoices or credit notes and entering in day books.

You are the bookkeeper at Oxley Retail Ltd. The supplier invoice below has been checked and authorised:

	£
Quinn Trading Ltd	
Invoice no: 49231	
To: Oxley Retail Ltd	
Date: 25 June 20-4	
5 barbecues at £210.50 each	1,052.50
VAT @ 20%	210.50
TOTAL	1,263.00
Payment by BACS preferred	

(a)   **You are to** record the invoice in the bookkeeping system by:
- selecting the correct daybook
- making the appropriate entries on the available line in the day book
- totalling the total, VAT and net columns

Daybook	✔
Sales day book	
Purchases returns day book	
Purchases day book	
Discounts received day book	

Date 20-4	Name	Invoice number	Total £	VAT £	Net £
2 June	Stanton & Co	3684	879.84	146.64	733.30
10 June	Quinn Trading Ltd	49175	1,315.80	219.30	1,096.50
12 June	Patel Supplies	P1079	746.94	124.49	622.45
20 June	Garcia Goods	GG/685	1,825.08	304.18	1,520.90
	TOTALS				

(b) You are the bookkeeper at Sutton Traders Limited. The goods returns note and credit note below relate to incorrect goods supplied by Lukac Limited.

Sutton Traders Ltd Goods Returns Note
To: Lukac Ltd 1 August 20-9 15 x Product 48 Returned as faulty £20 net each Credit requested

Lukac Ltd

Credit note: CN247
To: Sutton Enterprises Ltd
Date: 1 August 20-9

	£
15 x Product 48	250.00
VAT @ 20%	60.00
Total	310.00

Identify **three** discrepancies in the credit note:

Discrepancy	✔
Buyer details	
Quantity of goods	
Date of credit note	
Net amount	
VAT amount	
Total amount	

Task 6

This task is about processing payments to suppliers.

(a) Identify which document would be used for each of the purposes below.

Purpose	Document
A document issued by the seller to the buyer reducing the amount owing	
A document issued by the seller stating the amount owing and the terms of payment	
A document authorised and issued by the buyer and sent to the seller stating the goods required	

For the Documents column, choose from the following options (use each once only):

Purchase order
Credit note
Invoice

(b) You are the bookkeeper at Sabir Limited. It is the policy of Sabir Limited to check statements of account when they are received and to include in the payment only those transactions from the statement that are shown in the supplier's account in payables ledger.

The following is the supplier account activity from the digital bookkeeping system for Manners & Co:

Supplier activity report: Manners & Co				
Date 20-8	Details	Debit £	Credit £	Balance £
1 April	Balance b/f		2,045	2,045
3 April	Credit note CN 741	310		1,735
4 April	Bank payment	2,045		(310)
14 April	Invoice 3218		1,618	1,308
20 April	Invoice 3376		796	2,104
26 April	Invoice 3521		1,024	3,128

The statement of account from the supplier is on the next page. **You are to** identify the **three** items in the statement of account that should not be included in the payment because they are missing from the supplier activity report.

Manners & Co Thorpe Road, Underwood, UN2 5PA STATEMENT OF ACCOUNT: Sabir Ltd				
Date 20-8	Document number	Details	Amount £	✔
3 April	CN 741	Goods returned	−310	
14 April	3218	Goods	1,618	
20 April	3376	Goods	796	
22 April	3410	Goods	895	
26 April	3521	Goods	1,024	
18 April	CN 758	Goods returned	−110	
30 April	3652	Goods	1,214	

(c)   You are the bookkeeper at Dowson Limited. Today, 14 May 20-1, you have received the two invoices below from credit suppliers who offer a prompt payment discount.

Davenport Ltd Invoice no: 6748	
To: Dowson Ltd	
Date: 13 May 20-1	
	£
30 x Product 68 at £25 each	750.00
VAT @ 20%	150.00
TOTAL	900.00

Terms: 2.5% discount if payment received within 10 days of date of invoice

Kazeem Supplies Ltd Invoice no: 6749	
To: Dowson Ltd	
Date: 12 May 20-1	
	£
60 x Product 45 at £20 each	1,200.00
VAT @ 20%	240.00
TOTAL	1,440.00

Terms: 2% discount if payment received within 14 days of date of invoice

Calculate the amount to be paid to each supplier if the prompt payment discount is taken and identify the date by which the payments should be made (choose from the date options below).

Customer	£	Date
Davenport Ltd		
Kazeem Supplies Ltd		

Date options
14 May 20-1
22 May 20-1
23 May 20-1
26 May 20-1
27 May 20-1

Task 7

This task is about processing transactions in the cash book.

You are the bookkeeper at Blenheim Ltd.

The amount shown below has been received from customers and the transaction is ready to be entered into the cash book module of your digital bookkeeping system.

Receipt 481
5 June 20-8
Cash sales from customers:
Total £3,019.62 including VAT

(a) Make the necessary entries in the cash book by:

- selecting the correct side of the cash book
- choosing the description for the details column of the cash book
- recording the entry in the cash book

Cash book	✔
Cash book – receipts	
Cash book – payments	

Description for details column	✔
Total	
VAT	
Trade receivables	
Sales	

Date 20-8	Details	Total £	VAT £	Net £

(b) Identify which document you will refer to for details of payments to be recorded in the cash book.

Information required	Document
Details of payments made to credit suppliers	
Details of recurring payments made through the bank account	

Select your document from the following list: Cash sales receipts, Internet banking payments schedule, Paying-in slip counterfoils, Sales invoices, Standing order and direct debit schedule.

Task 8

This task is about processing transactions in the petty cash book.

You are the bookkeeper at Elmhurst Supplies Ltd and you are dealing with the analysed petty cash book.

Today is 30 June 20-2 and there is one last petty cash payment for the month to be recorded: an amount of £19.02 including VAT has been paid for stationery.

(a) Calculate the VAT and net amounts to be recorded in the petty cash book.

VAT £	Net £

Before the petty cash payment in (a) was recorded, the stationery analysis column totalled £45.21.

(b) Calculate the total of the stationery analysis column after the payment in (a) is recorded.

£ [   ]

After all the June petty cash payments have been recorded, an amount of £22.36 is left in the petty cash float. The petty cash float is then topped up to the imprest amount of £250.

(c) What will be the entry in the petty cash book to record this transaction?

Details	Amount £	Debit ✔	Credit ✔

Select your details from the following list: Bank, Cash receipt, Cash sales, Credit sales, Payables, Receivables.

Task 9

This task is about processing recurring entries.

You are the cashier at Kelly Ltd. Today, 1 April 20-6, you are setting up a recurring payment in the cash book module of your digital bookkeeping system.

Standing order and direct debit schedule:

> Kelly Ltd has signed a contract for a year to rent additional office space from Albion Ltd at a cost of £800 per month (no VAT). Date of first payment: 1 April 20-6.
>
> A standing order authority has been set up with the bank.

Show the necessary entries in the cash book by:

- selecting the correct side of the cash book
- recording the entry in the cash book (choose Details and Frequency from the options below)

Cash book	✔
Cash book – receipts	
Cash book – payments	

Date 20-6	Details	Total £	VAT £	Net £	Frequency	Recurrences

Details	✔
Rent paid	
Rent received	
Cash payments	
Office equipment	

Frequency	✔
Daily	
Weekly	
Monthly	
Annually	

Task 10

This task is about transferring data from the books of prime entry.

The totals of the sales returns day book at the end of the month are as follows:

Details	Total £	VAT £	Net £
Total for month	594	99	495

(a) Show the entries to be made in the general ledger.

Account name	Amount £	Debit ✔	Credit ✔

Select your account name from the following list: Discounts allowed, Discounts received, Payables ledger control, Purchases, Purchases returns, Receivables ledger control, Sales, Sales returns, VAT.

An entry in the discounts received day book is for a credit note received from Mansi Ltd for £55 plus VAT.

(b) Show the entry in the payables ledger.

Account name	Amount £	Debit ✔	Credit ✔

Select your account name from the following list: Discounts allowed, Discounts received, Mansi Ltd, Payables ledger control, Purchases, Purchases returns, Receivables ledger control, Sales, Sales returns, VAT.

Task 11

This task is about totalling and balancing ledger accounts.

The following account is in the general ledger at the close of day on 30 June 20-1:

Office equipment

20-1	Details	Amount £	20-1	Details	Amount £
1 Jun	Balance b/f	4,580	15 Jun	Bank	425
25 Jun	Bank	1,250			

(a) • What is the balance brought down at 1 July on the account?

• Indicate whether the balance brought down is debit or credit.

Account name	Balance £	Debit ✔	Credit ✔
Office equipment			

(b) The following account is in the payables ledger at the close of the financial year on 30 April 20-1:

20-1	Details	Amount £	20-1	Details	Amount £
12 April	Bank	2,712	1 April	Balance b/f	3,409
18 April	Purchases Returns	138	24 April	Purchases	1,284
	Total			Total	

Complete the account by:

• inserting the balance carried down, together with date and details
• inserting the totals
• inserting the balance brought down, together with date and details

Note:

• for the Details column, choose from: Balance b/d, Balance c/d, Difference
• for the Date column, choose from: 1 April, 30 April, 1 May, 31 May

Practice assessment 2

Assessment information

- This practice assessment contains **11 tasks** and you should attempt to complete **every** task.
- Each task is independent. You will not need to refer to your answers from previous tasks.
- Read every task carefully to make sure you understand what is required.
- Where the date is relevant, it is given in the task data.
- Both minus signs and brackets can be used to indicate negative numbers **unless** task instructions state otherwise.
- You must use a full stop to indicate a decimal point. For example, write 100.57, **not** 100,57 or 10057.
- You may use a comma to indicate a number in the thousands, but you don't have to. For example, 10000 and 10,000 are both acceptable.
- Mathematical rounding should be applied where appropriate.

Scenario

The tasks in this practice assessment are set in different business situations where the following apply:

- Businesses use a variety of bookkeeping systems.
- Double entry takes place in the general ledger.
- The VAT rate is 20%.

Task 1

This task is about manual and digital bookkeeping systems.

(a) Identify which document/record would be used for each of the purposes below.

Purpose	Document/Record
To list account balances in order to check that the value of debit entries and credit entries is equal	
The first place to record financial documents in the accounting system	
To record cash payments for small purchases and small payments	
To locate the accounting records of individual suppliers who supply on credit to the business	
To tell the business how much is owing from all its customers	

For the documents/records, choose from the following options (use each once only):

Petty cash book
Receivables ledger control account
Book of prime entry
Payables ledger
Trial balance

(b)   A business uses the following coding system for its products:

- first two letters of the product type

- first two letters of the product colour

- a number which follows sequentially for each new product

The most recent product code is shown in the table which follows.

You are to create a code for each of the two new products.

Date 20-2	Product	Produce code
12 Feb	Envelopes, white	ENWH84
14 Feb	Folders, green	
16 Feb	Pens, red	

(c)   The following statements are about manual bookkeeping systems.

Identify whether each is TRUE or FALSE.

Statement	True ✔	False ✔
Payables ledger control account is a book of prime entry		
The statement of profit or loss gives a 'snapshot' of the assets, liabilities and capital of a business at a particular date		

(d)   The following statements are about digital bookkeeping systems.

Identify whether each is TRUE or FALSE.

Statement	True ✔	False ✔
The transfer of data into the control accounts is automatic		
Duplication of transactions is prevented		

Task 2

This task is about principles of double-entry bookkeeping.

(a) The following accounts are in the bookkeeping system.

Identify the classification of each account.

Account	Classification
Rent received	
Vehicles	
Payables	
Bank charges	

Options
Asset
Liability
Income
Expense

(b) The asset accounts total £180,243 and the liability accounts total £89,627.

What is the amount of capital (do NOT use a minus sign or brackets)?

£ [   ]

(c) Identify the dual effect on double-entry bookkeeping of the following transactions (ignore VAT):

Transaction	Dual effect
Purchased office equipment using a bank overdraft	
Owner transfers a vehicle into the business	
Trade payables account settled using a bank overdraft	
Bank loan repaid from cash at bank	
Trade receivable's account settled in cash	

For the dual effect, choose from the following options (use each once only):

Increase in asset and liability
Decrease in asset and liability
Increase in asset and capital
Increase and decrease of assets
Increase and decrease of liabilities

Task 3

This task is about processing customer invoices or credit notes and entering in day books.

(a) You are the bookkeeper at Groves Ltd and are preparing sales invoice number 4576 from the delivery note below. The customer benefits from a 5% trade discount.

Groves Ltd
Delivery note: DN6815

To: Okeze Ltd
Customer ref: OK03
Date: 8 June 20-4

1,000 units of product G331.
Price before discount £2.40 per unit, plus VAT.

Calculate the amount to be included in the invoice.

	£
Amount before discount	
Trade discount	
Amount after discount	
VAT at 20%	
Total	

(b) **You are to** record the invoice in the digital bookkeeping system by:

- identifying the correct daybook
- completing the necessary entries in the day book

Daybook	✔
Sales day book	
Sales returns day book	
Purchases day book	
Purchases returns day book	
Discounts allowed day book	
Discounts received day book	

Date 20-4	Customer code	Customer	Invoice number	Total £	VAT £	Net £	G330 £	G331 £	G332 £
8 June	OK03	Okeze Ltd	4576						

Task 4

This task is about processing receipts from customers.

(a)   You are the bookkeeper at HPL Ltd. Today you have received a bank transfer for £2,149.04 from Sutton plc in full settlement of the two invoices and the credit note shown below.

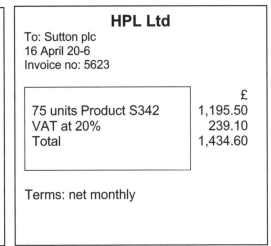

HPL Ltd	
To: Sutton plc 4 April 20-6 Invoice no: 5491	
	£
65 units Product P105	802.10
VAT at 20%	160.42
Total	962.52
Terms: net monthly	

HPL Ltd	
To: Sutton plc 16 April 20-6 Invoice no: 5623	
	£
75 units Product S342	1,195.50
VAT at 20%	239.10
Total	1,434.60
Terms: net monthly	

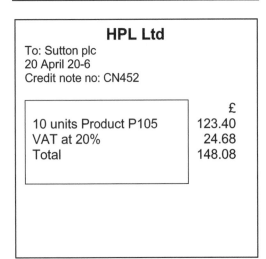

HPL Ltd	
To: Sutton plc 20 April 20-6 Credit note no: CN452	
	£
10 units Product P105	123.40
VAT at 20%	24.68
Total	148.08

Complete the following statements about the accuracy of the amount received by selecting the appropriate option.

Sutton plc has ....

underpaid the amount owing
overpaid the amount owing
paid the correct amount

> This means that ....

a request for a further payment should be made
there is no balance outstanding
a refund should be offered

(b) HPL Ltd has offered a customer a 2.5% discount for payment of all the outstanding invoices detailed below, by the end of the week.

Calculate the amount that should be paid by the end of the week to settle:

- each invoice
- the total of all invoices

Outstanding invoices	Total £	VAT £	Net £	Amount to be paid £
5635	2,814	469	2,345	
5682	1,290	215	1,075	
5705	1,020	170	850	
			Total	

(c) HPL Ltd has received a bank transfer for £2,566.70 and the remittance advice below from a customer. The customer's terms of payment are net monthly.

Remittance advice	
Invoice	**£**
5368	532.50
5404	1,076.20
5502	439.60
5610	518.40
Total	**2,566.70**

The policy of HPL Ltd is to allocate any underpayment as a part payment and to query any overpayment.

From the customer report below, allocate the amount received by selecting the appropriate action.

Transaction	Details	Amount £	Action
Balance b/f		1,608.70	
Invoice 5502	Delivery note 6271	493.60	
Invoice 5610	Delivery note 6742	638.40	
Credit note 491	Overcharge re invoice 5610	120.00	

Select your options from: Allocate full amount, Allocate part payment, Query overpayment.

Task 5

This task is about processing supplier invoices or credit notes and entering in day books.

(a)   You are the bookkeeper at Sutton Retail Ltd. The supplier invoice below has been checked, authorised and coded:

Kumar Ltd
Invoice no: 27451

To: Sutton Retail Ltd
Date: 10 April 20-2

	£
8 garden seat sets at £195.50 each	1,564.00
VAT @ 20%	312.80
TOTAL	1,876.80

Terms: Net monthly

Checked by: DC   General ledger code: 4174
Authorised by: JC   Supplier code: KU02

You are to enter the invoice in the digital bookkeeping system by:

- selecting the correct module option
- making the necessary entries

Module option	✔
Sales day book	
Sales returns day book	
Purchases day book	
Purchases returns day book	
Discounts allowed day book	
Discounts received day book	

Date 20-2	Supplier code	Supplier	General ledger code	Invoice number	Net £	VAT code
10 April		Kumar Ltd				

Select your VAT code from the following: VAT1 (Exempt), VAT2 (0%), VAT3 (5%), VAT4 (20%).

(b) The purchase order and invoice below relate to goods supplied by Elmhurst Products.

<table>
<tr><td>

Sutton Retail Ltd

Purchase order no: PO5721
To: Elmhurst Products
11 April 20-2

20 x Product Y341
Agreed price: £22.41 each
Agreed terms: Net 30 days

</td><td>

Elmhurst Products

Invoice no: E3764
To: Sutton Retail Ltd
Date: 15 April 20-2

	£
20 x Product Y314 at £22.41 each	448.20
VAT @ 20%	99.64
Total	348.56

Terms of payment: Net 14 days

</td></tr>
</table>

Identify **four** discrepancies in the invoice:

Discrepancy	✔
Quantity supplied	
Product supplied	
Date of invoice	
Unit price	
Net amount	
VAT amount	
Total amount	
Terms of payment	

Task 6

This task is about processing payments to suppliers.

(a)   An invoice dated 10 April has been received from a supplier for £7,080 including VAT. The supplier's terms of payment are:

- 30 days net, or

- 2% discount for payment received within 20 days of date of invoice, or

- 3% discount for payment received within 10 days of date of invoice

(i)   Identify the date by which the supplier should receive payment if no discount is taken.

Date	✔
20 April	
30 April	
10 May	
11 May	
20 May	
31 May	

(ii)   Identify the amount to be paid, and the date by which the supplier should receive payment, for each of the terms of payment offered below.

Terms of payment	Amount to be paid £	Date by which supplier should receive payment
Payment within 20 days		
Payment within 10 days		

For the date, choose from the following options:

Options
20 April
30 April
10 May
11 May
20 May
31 May

(b) A statement of account received from another supplier, Southern Suppliers, does not reconcile with the supplier report below. The statement of account shows an amount outstanding of £12,141. This amount does not include the two bank payments made on 29 April and 30 April which were received by the supplier after the statement had been prepared.

Identify which FOUR amounts were included in the two bank payments by ticking against the appropriate amounts.

Supplier report Southern Suppliers				
Date 20-3	Transaction type	Details	£	✔
1 April	BAL	Balance b/f	4,512	
2 April	SCN	Credit note 1217	238	
10 April	SI	Invoice 4538	1,726	
12 April	SI	Invoice 4603	2,134	
18 April	SI	Invoice 4725	896	
20 April	SI	Invoice 4812	1,522	
22 April	SI	Invoice 4867	943	
25 April	SI	Invoice 4938	646	
29 April	BP	Bank payment 074324	4,274	
30 April	BP	Bank payment 074327	3,656	

(c) Calculate the amount that should be paid to settle the balance remaining on the account.

£ [   ]

Task 7

This task is about processing transactions in the cash book.

You are the bookkeeper at Wentworth Ltd.

The two amounts shown below have been received and the transactions are ready to be entered into the cash book module of your digital bookkeeping system.

Wyvern Agency **Payment: 574** **Date:** 2 May 20-3	
Rent of office for May 20-3 Exempt from VAT Bank payment made today	£600.00

Nelson & Co **Payment: 621** **Date:** 2 May 20-3	
	£
Goods supplied on credit VAT at 20%	346.50 69.30
Cheque enclosed	415.80

(a) Enter the transactions in the digital bookkeeping system by:

- selecting the correct module option
- choosing the general ledger code and the VAT code for the cash book
- recording the necessary entries

Module option	✔
Cash book – receipts	
Cash book – payments	
Petty cash book – receipts	
Petty cash book – payments	

Choose your general ledger code and VAT code from the following:

General ledger code
3100 Trade payables
3600 Trade receivables
6050 Rent received
7280 Cash sales

VAT code
VAT1 Exempt
VAT2 0%
VAT3 5%
VAT4 20%

Date 20-3	Details	General ledger code	Document number	Net £	VAT code
2 May	Wyvern Agency		574		
2 May	Nelson & Co		621		

(b) At the end of the month, the debit side of the cash book totalled £14,705.33 and the credit side totalled £16,210.85.

Calculate the bank balance, using a minus sign if your calculations indicate an overdrawn bank balance (eg -476).

£ [   ]

Task 8

This task is about processing transactions in the petty cash book.

You are the bookkeeper at AQ Products Ltd. The company keeps an analysed petty cash book, which uses the non-imprest system. On the first day of each month, the petty cash float is topped up with a withdrawal of £250 from the bank.

On 1 April 20-2, before the top up from the bank, there was £25.47 in the petty cash box. During April, petty cash payments totalled £204.68.

(a) Identify the entry required in the petty cash book to record the closing balance on 30 April 20-2.

Details	Amount £	Debit ✔	Credit ✔

For the details column, choose from:

Balance carried down
Balance brought down

(b) The first petty cash transaction in May is shown below:

Petty cash voucher No: 181
1 May 20-2
Stationery from Office Supplies Ltd £24.78 including VAT
Receipt attached

Complete the entry in the petty cash book.

Date 20-2	Details	Total £	VAT £	Net £
1 May	Office Supplies Ltd			

Task 9

This task is about processing recurring entries.

You are the bookkeeper at Tomlin Trading Limited. The accountant has emailed you with details of a new bank payment that she has authorised, today, as follows:

Email
I have authorised the following recurring bank payments for the maintenance of our office equipment: Payee: Vale Services Limited, sort code 20-18-34, account number 10045671 Amount: £65.50, plus VAT at 20% per month for 12 months First payment on 10 May 20-3 and 10th monthly thereafter Sonya Holmes, Accountant 1 May 20-3

Set up the recurring entry in the cash book module of your digital bookkeeping system by completing the table below (choose Dates, Details, Frequency and VAT code from the options below):

Transaction type: Recurring payment	
Details	
Payee	Vale Services Limited
Sort code	20-18-34
Account number	10045671
Start date	
Frequency	
Recurrences	
End date	
Amount	
VAT code	

Dates		Details	
1 May 20-3		230 Bank	
10 May 20-3		240 Cash	
10 April 20-4		460 Office expenses	
10 May 20-4		480 General Expenses	

Frequency		VAT code	
Weekly		VAT1 Exempt	
Monthly		VAT2 0%	
Quarterly		VAT3 5%	
Annually		VAT4 20%	

Task 10

This task is about transferring data from the books of prime entry.

The totals of the purchases returns day book at the end of the month are as follows:

Details	Total £	VAT £	Net £
Totals	787.20	131.20	656.00

(a) Show the entries to be made in the general ledger.

Account name	Amount £	Debit ✔	Credit ✔
Purchases returns			
VAT			
Payables ledger control			

The discounts allowed day book has been totalled and all amounts have been transferred to the relevant general ledger accounts. One of the transactions relates to a credit note for £47 plus VAT issued to Gomez Ltd.

(b) Identify the ledger in which the credit note will be entered.

Ledger	✔
Payables	
Receivables	

(c) Enter the credit note in the ledger.

Account name	Amount £	Debit ✔	Credit ✔

Select your account name from the following list: Discounts allowed, Discounts received, Gomez Ltd, Payables ledger control, Purchases, Purchases returns, Receivables ledger control, Sales, Sales returns, VAT.

Task 11

This task is about totalling and balancing ledger accounts.

The following account is ready to be totalled and balanced at the end of June 20-2:

20-2	Details	Amount £	20-2	Details	Amount £
1 June	Balance b/f	1,407	12 June	Bank	855
16 June	Sales	691			
	Total			Total	

(a) Identify the entry required to record the closing balance on 30 June 20-2:

Details	Amount £	Debit ✔	Credit ✔

For the Details column, choose from: Balance b/d, Balance c/d, Difference.

(b) Calculate the total that will be entered in both the debit and credit column after the closing balance has been recorded.

£ [   ]

The following two accounts are in the ledgers at close of day on 30 June 20-2:

Account RL130

20-2	Details	Amount £	20-2	Details	Amount £
3 June	Sales	1,076	20 June	Bank	895
15 June	Sales	155			

Account PL235

20-2	Details	Amount £	20-2	Details	Amount £
8 June	Bank	641	18 June	Purchases	87
			25 June	Purchases	822

(c) Identify the entries required to record the opening balance of each account on 1 July 20-2:

Account code	Details	Amount £	Debit ✔	Credit ✔
RL130				
PL235				

For the Details column, choose from: Balance b/d, Balance c/d, Difference.

Practice assessment 3

Assessment information

•   This practice assessment contains **11 tasks** and you should attempt to complete **every** task.

•   Each task is independent. You will not need to refer to your answers from previous tasks.

•   Read every task carefully to make sure you understand what is required.

•   Where the date is relevant, it is given in the task data.

•   Both minus signs and brackets can be used to indicate negative numbers **unless** task instructions state otherwise.

•   You must use a full stop to indicate a decimal point. For example, write 100.57, **not** 100,57 or 10057.

•   You may use a comma to indicate a number in the thousands, but you don't have to. For example, 10000 and 10,000 are both acceptable.

•   Mathematical rounding should be applied where appropriate.

Scenario

The tasks in this practice assessment are set in different business situations where the following apply:

•   Businesses use a variety of bookkeeping systems.
•   Double entry takes place in the general ledger.
•   The VAT rate is 20%.

Task 1

This task is about manual and digital bookkeeping systems.

(a)   Identify which document or record would be used for each of the purposes below.

Purpose	Document/Record
Detailing credit customer transactions and issued, often at the month-end, to encourage payment of amounts owing	
Detailing all general ledger debit and credit balances which are totalled to give a preliminary check of the accuracy of the bookkeeping system	
Detailing goods which have been returned by credit customers and which gives a reduction in the amount owing to the seller	
Detailing the payment of low-value business expenses made in cash for a period, often a month, the balance of which is topped up from the bank	

For the document/record, choose from the following options (use each once only):

Statement of account
Petty cash book
Credit note
Trial balance

(b) The digital bookkeeping system that you use creates alphanumerical customer codes using the following format:

First two letters of customer name/three numerical digits

The current customer accounts in the receivables ledger are:

Customer name	Customer account code
Burt Builders	BU001
Collet & Co	CO001
Green Ltd	GR002
Groves & Co	GR001
Paul & Paul	PA001
Stanton Supplies	ST001

Two new customer accounts shown below need to be coded.

Enter the relevant account codes for each that the digital bookkeeping system will create.

Customer name	Customer account code
Grundy Goods	
Stewart Ltd	

(c) Identify the book of prime entry being described in the statement below.

A day book detailing items bought on credit from suppliers

	✔
Purchases day book	
Purchases returns day book	
Sales day book	
Sales returns day book	
Cash book	

(d) Identify whether each of the following statements regarding bookkeeping systems is true or false.

Statement	True ✔	False ✔
Receivables ledger control account shows the total amount owing to suppliers		
The owner's capital account always has a credit balance		
A trial balance that balances proves that the bookkeeping is accurate		

Task 2

This task is about principles of double-entry bookkeeping.

(a) The following accounts are in the bookkeeping system.

Classify each account as an asset, a liability, income or an expense.

Account	Asset ✔	Liability ✔	Income ✔	Expense ✔
Rent received				
Office equipment				
Payables				
Wages and salaries				

(b) The income accounts total £95,625 and the expense accounts total £73,854. Calculate the amount of profit or loss (for a loss, use a minus sign or brackets).

£ [   ]

(c) The transactions below have been entered into the bookkeeping system. Identify the dual effect of each transaction by choosing the appropriate description from the list below – use each once only. You should ignore VAT in this task.

Transaction	Dual effect
Owner pays money into the bank to reduce the bank overdraft	
Bank payment made from overdrawn bank account to settle payables' accounts	
Purchased office equipment on credit from Wyvern Office Limited	
Old office equipment sold for cash	
A receivables account is settled by cheque which is paid into the bank to reduce the overdraft	

Increase in both an asset and a liability
Decrease in both an asset and a liability
Increase and decrease in an asset
Increase and decrease in a liability
Increase in capital and decrease in a liability

Task 3

This task is about processing customer invoices or credit notes and entering in day books.

You are preparing sales credit note number CN 247 from the goods received note below. The customer benefits from a 5% bulk discount.

Antu Ltd
Goods received note: GRN 482

1 June 20-7
The following goods have been returned today in good condition from Goode Ltd (customer code GO02).

600 units of Product T115 returned as they are not as ordered.

Price before discount £2.55 per unit, plus VAT.

(a) Calculate the amounts to be included in the credit note.

	£
Amount before discount	
Bulk discount	
Amount after discount	
VAT at 20%	
Total	

(b) Identify the day book in which the credit note will be entered.

Daybook	✔
Sales day book	
Sales returns day book	
Purchases day book	
Purchases returns day book	
Discounts allowed day book	
Discounts received day book	

(c) Complete the entry in the day book.

Date 20-4	Customer code	Customer	Invoice number	Total £	VAT £	Net £	T110 £	T115 £	T120 £
1 June	GO02	Goode Ltd	CN 247						

Task 4

This task is about processing receipts from customers.

You are the bookkeeper at Tamayo Trading. A receipt of £7,012 has been received from a credit customer, King Limited. The following is an extract for King Limited from your bookkeeping system, together with the remittance advice.

June sales list: King Ltd		
Date **20-5**	**Details**	**Amount** **£**
3 June	Invoice 5042	3,068
10 June	Credit note 92	−165
21 June	Invoice 5738	2,465
25 June	Credit note 104	−79
30 June	Invoice 6014	1,411

Remittance Advice: King Ltd To: Tamayo Trading 30 June 20-5		
Date **20-6**	**Details**	**Amount** **£**
3 June	Invoice 5142	3,068
10 June	Credit note 92	165
12 June	Invoice 5738	2,465
25 June	Credit note 104	−97
30 June	Invoice 6014	1,411
TOTAL: Paid by BACS 30 June		7,012

(a) You are to identify the discrepancies (if any) between the transactions from the sales list and the transactions in the remittance advice.

20-5	Details	£	Discrepancies
3 June	Invoice 5042	3,068	
10 June	Credit note 92	−165	
21 June	Invoice 5738	2,465	
25 June	Credit note 104	−79	
30 June	Invoice 6014	1,411	

For the discrepancies column, choose from the following options (use each once only):

No discrepancy
Incorrect date
Incorrect invoice number
Incorrectly recorded
Incorrect amount

(b) What will be the balance of King Limited's account after the payment of £7,012 has been allocated to its account?

Balance of King Ltd's receivables account	✔
(a) £312 underpaid	
(b) £312 overpaid	
(c) £79 underpaid	
(d) £79 overpaid	

(c) An invoice to supply goods for £1,728 including VAT has been sent by Tamayo Trading to Kassir Limited offering prompt payment discount of 2% for payment within 10 days.

What will be the amount received by Tamayo Trading if Kassir Limited pays within 10 days?

£

(d) The following remittance advice has been received by Tamayo Trading from Chedzoy & Co:

<table>
<tr><td colspan="2" align="center">Chedzoy & Co</td></tr>
<tr><td colspan="2">BACS remittance advice
To: Tamayo Trading
Date: 30 June 20-5
Amount: £1,932
Detail:
<ul>
<li>£1,000 part payment of balance at 1 June 20-5</li>
<li>£932 part payment of invoice 5431</li>
<li>Full allocation of credit note 105 to invoice 5431</li>
</ul>
</td></tr>
</table>

You are to show the outstanding amount for each entry after the remittance has been allocated.

Date 20-5	Detail	£	Outstanding amount £
1 June	Opening balance	1,822	
10 June	Invoice 5431	1,027	
25 June	Credit note 105	−95	

Task 5

This task is about processing supplier invoices or credit notes and entering in day books.

(a) You are the bookkeeper at Davies Retail Ltd. The supplier invoice below has been checked, authorised and coded:

Wright Ltd
Invoice no: 35472

To: Davies Retail Ltd
Date: 12 October 20-8

	£
50 artificial Christmas trees at £30.75 each	1,537.50
VAT @ 20%	307.50
TOTAL	1,845.00

Terms: Net monthly

Checked by: MLC   General ledger code: 5176
Authorised by: LCH   Supplier code: WR001

You are to enter the invoice in the digital bookkeeping system by:

- selecting the correct module option
- making the necessary entries

Module option	✔
Sales day book	
Sales returns day book	
Purchases day book	
Purchases returns day book	
Discounts allowed day book	
Discounts received day book	

Date 20-8	Supplier code	Supplier	General ledger code	Invoice number	Net £	VAT code
12 Oct		Wright Ltd				

Select your VAT code from the following: VAT1 (Exempt), VAT2 (0%), VAT3 (5%), VAT4 (20%).

(b)   The purchase order and invoice below relate to goods supplied by Prime Products.

<table>
<tr><td>

Davies Retail Ltd

Purchase order no: PO4728
To: Prime Products
14 October 20-8

150 x Product PP365
Agreed price: £12.45 each
Agreed terms: Net monthly

</td><td>

Prime Products
Invoice no: P2461
To: Davies Retail Ltd
Date: 14 October 20-8

	£
100 x Product PP365 at £12.55 each	1,255.00
VAT @ 20%	251.00
Total	1,004.00

Terms of payment: Net 14 days

</td></tr>
</table>

Identify **four** discrepancies in the invoice:

Discrepancy	✔
Quantity supplied	
Product supplied	
Date of invoice	
Unit price	
Net amount	
VAT amount	
Total amount	
Terms of payment	

Task 6

This task is about processing payments to suppliers.

(a) Identify which document would be used for each of the purposes below.

Purpose	Document
A document issued by the seller stating the cost at which goods or services can be provided	
A document issued by the seller listing the goods and accompanying them	
A document issued by the seller listing invoices, credit notes and payments on the account and stating a total amount due	

For the Document column, choose from the following options (use each once only):

Delivery note
Quotation
Statement of account

(b) You are the bookkeeper at Sebright Limited. It is the policy of Sebright Limited to check statements of account when they are received and to include in the payment only those transactions from the statement that are shown on the supplier's account in payables ledger.

The following is the supplier account activity for Marr & Co from the digital bookkeeping system:

Supplier activity report: Marr & Co				
Date 20-6	Details	Debit £	Credit £	Balance £
1 May	Balance b/f		1,065	1,065
3 May	Credit note CN 481	134		931
4 May	Bank payment	1,065		(134)
14 May	Invoice 4785		1,428	1,294
20 May	Invoice 4896		867	2,161
26 May	Invoice 5211		2,013	4,174

The statement of account from the supplier is on the next page. **You are to** identify the **three** items in the statement of account that should not be included in the payment because they are missing from the supplier activity report.

Marr & Co Wills Road, Wyvern WV1 3QX STATEMENT OF ACCOUNT: Sebright Ltd				
Date 20-6	Document number	Details	Amount £	✔
3 May	CN 481	Goods returned	−134	
14 May	SI 4785	Goods	1,428	
20 May	SI 4896	Goods	867	
22 May	SI 4945	Goods	1,045	
26 May	SI 5211	Goods	2,013	
18 May	CN 502	Goods returned	−85	
30 May	SI5652	Goods	1,319	

(c) You are the bookkeeper at Keyte Limited. Today, 14 May 20-6 you have received the two invoices below from credit suppliers who offer a prompt payment discount.

Castille Ltd
Invoice no: 7381

To: Keyte Ltd
Date: 13 May 20-6

	£
40 x Product 61 at £15 each	600.00
VAT @ 20%	120.00
TOTAL	720.00

Terms: 3% discount if payment received within 14 days of date of invoice

Savin Supplies Ltd
Invoice no: SI 4731

To: Keyte Ltd
Date: 12 May 20-6

	£
30 x Product 18 at £14 each	420.00
VAT @ 20%	84.00
TOTAL	504.00

Terms: 2.5% discount if payment received within 10 days of date of invoice

Calculate the amount to be paid to each supplier if the prompt payment discount is taken, and identify the date by which the payments should be made (choose from the date options below).

Customer	£	Date
Castille Ltd		
Savin Supplies Ltd		

Date options	
14 May 20-6	26 May 20-6
22 May 20-6	27 May 20-6
23 May 20-6	

Task 7

This task is about processing transactions in the cash book.

You are the bookkeeper at Laceby Ltd.

The two amounts shown below have been paid today and the transactions are ready to be entered into the cash book module of your digital bookkeeping system.

Laceby Ltd	
Remittance: 341	
To: Blenheim Lettings	
Date: 11 August 20-7	
Rent of office for August 20-7 Exempt from VAT	£800.00
Bank payment made today	

Laceby Ltd	
Remittance: 342	
To: Martin's Garage Ltd	
Date: 11 August 20-7	
	£
Repairs to delivery van	451.60
VAT at 20%	90.32
Cheque enclosed	541.92

(a) Enter the transactions in the digital bookkeeping system by:

- selecting the correct module option
- choosing the general ledger code and the VAT code for the cash book
- recording the necessary entries

Module option	✔
Cash book – receipts	
Cash book – payments	
Petty cash book – receipts	
Petty cash book – payments	

Choose your general ledger code and VAT code from the following:

General ledger code
3100 Trade payables
3600 Trade receivables
6100 Rent paid
7280 Vehicle repairs

VAT code
VAT1 Exempt
VAT2 0%
VAT3 5%
VAT4 20%

Date 20-7	Details	General ledger code	Document number	Net £	VAT code
11 Aug	Blenheim Lettings		341		
11 Aug	Martin's Garage Ltd		342		

(b)   At the end of the month, the debit side of the cash book totalled £10,385.96 and the credit side totalled £8,346.19.

Calculate the bank balance, using a minus sign if your calculations indicate an overdrawn bank balance (eg –476).

£ [   ]

Task 8

This task is about processing transactions in the petty cash book.

You are the bookkeeper at Sydney Supplies Ltd and you are dealing with the analysed petty cash book.

Today is 30 April 20-4 and there is one last petty cash payment for the month to be recorded: an amount of £12.60 including VAT has been paid for a taxi fare.

(a) Calculate the VAT and net amounts to be recorded in the petty cash book.

VAT £	Net £

Before the petty cash payment in (a) was recorded, the travel expenses analysis column totalled £63.42.

(b) Calculate the total of the travel expenses analysis column after the payment in (a) is recorded.

£ [   ]

After all the April petty cash payments have been recorded, an amount of £35.43 is left in the petty cash float. The petty cash float is then topped up to the imprest amount of £200.

(c) What will be the entry in the petty cash book to record this transaction?

Details	Amount £	Debit ✔	Credit ✔

Select your details from the following list: Bank, Cash receipt, Cash sales, Credit sales, Payables, Receivables.

Task 9

This task is about processing recurring entries.

You are the cashier at Farias Ltd. Today, 1 June 20-3, you are setting up a recurring payment in the cash book module of your digital bookkeeping system.

Standing order and direct debit schedule:

Farias Ltd has signed a contract for a year for office cleaning with Spick 'n Span Ltd at a cost of £1,150 per month (plus VAT). Date of first payment: 1 June 20-3.

A standing order authority has been set up with the bank.

Show the necessary entries in the cash book by:

• selecting the correct side of the cash book

• recording the entry in the cash book (choose Details and Frequency from the options below)

Cash book	✔
Cash book – receipts	
Cash book – payments	

Date 20-3	Details	Total £	VAT £	Net £	Frequency	Recurrences

Details	✔
Stationery	
Cleaning	
Cash payments	
Office equipment	

Frequency	✔
Daily	
Weekly	
Monthly	
Annually	

Task 10

This task is about transferring data from the books of prime entry.

The totals of the sales day book at the end of the month are as follows:

Details	Total £	VAT £	Net £
Total for month	8,190	1,365	6,825

(a)   Show the entries to be made in the general ledger.

Account name		Amount £	Debit ✔	Credit ✔

Select your account name from the following list: Discounts allowed, Discounts received, Payables ledger control, Purchases, Purchases returns, Receivables ledger control, Sales, Sales returns, VAT.

An entry in the discounts allowed day book is for a credit note issued to Nelson Ltd for £35 plus VAT.

(b)   Show the entry in the receivables ledger.

Account name		Amount £	Debit ✔	Credit ✔

Select your account name from the following list: Discounts allowed, Discounts received, Nelson Ltd, Payables ledger control, Purchases, Purchases returns, Receivables ledger control, Sales, Sales returns, VAT.

Task 11

This task is about totalling and balancing ledger accounts.

The following account is ready to be totalled and balanced at the end of October 20-1:

20-1	Details	Amount £	20-1	Details	Amount £
5 Oct	Bank	742	1 Oct	Balance b/f	1,386
			1 Oct	Purchases	958
	Total			Total	

(a) Identify the entry required to record the closing balance on 31 October 20-1:

Details	Amount £	Debit ✔	Credit ✔

For the Details column, choose from: Balance b/d, Balance c/d, Difference.

(b) Calculate the total that will be entered in both the debit and credit column after the closing balance has been recorded.

£ [   ]

The following two accounts are in the ledgers at close of day on 31 October 20-1:

Account RL640

20-1	Details	Amount £	20-1	Details	Amount £
3 Oct	Sales	1,422	20 Oct	Bank	1,106
15 Oct	Sales	68			

Account RL1050

20-1	Details	Amount £	20-1	Details	Amount £
8 Oct	Bank	590	18 Oct	Purchases	102
			25 Oct	Purchases	1,055

(c) Identify the entries required to record the opening balance of each account on 1 November 20-1:

Account code	Details	Amount £	Debit ✔	Credit ✔
RL640				
PL1050				

For the Details column, choose from: Balance b/d, Balance c/d, Difference.

Answers to practice assessment 1

Task 1

(a)

Purpose	Document
Detailing a bank payment to a supplier	Remittance advice
Detailing bank receipts and payments for a given period, together with the bank balance or overdraft	Bank statement
Detailing a low value payment made in cash for a business expense	Petty cash voucher
Detailing goods or services supplied by a seller to a buyer and indicating the amount owed and the required payment date	Invoice

(b)

Customer name	Customer account code
Allied Stores	AALI02
Traditional Builders	TRAD03

(c)

	✔
Purchases day book	
Purchases returns day book	✔
Sales day book	
Sales returns day book	
Cash book	

(d)

Statement	True ✔	False ✔
A manual bookkeeping system is always completely accurate		✔
A digital bookkeeping system enables electronic recording of purchases invoices, with automatic updating of accounts in the payables ledger	✔	
A digital bookkeeping system allows reports, such as a trial balance, to be available on demand	✔	

Task 2

(a)

Assets £	Liabilities £	Capital £
32,451.68	18,727.27	13,724.41

(b)

Transaction	Dual effect
Owner transfers a computer into the business	Increase in asset and capital
A bank loan has been received to pay for new office equipment	Increase in asset and liability
Settled a payable's account using the bank overdraft	Increase and decrease of liabilities
A receivable settles her account in cash	Increase and decrease of assets
Old office equipment sold for cash	Increase and decrease of assets

(c)

	✔
Rent paid	
Rent received	✔
Office expenses	
Sales	

Task 3

(a)

	✔
encourage them to pay early	
encourage business customers to buy regularly	✔

(b)

Daybook	✔
Sales day book	✔
Sales returns day book	
Purchases day book	
Discounts allowed day book	

Date 20-3	Name	Account code	Invoice number	Total £	VAT £	Net £
10 Jun	Malvern Autos	MALV01	47124	144.00	24.00	120.00

(c)

Purchases: engine oil	
Sales: car polish	
Sales: engine oil	✔
Sales: brake fluid	

(d)

As a debit entry	
As a credit entry	✔

Task 4

(a)

20-4	Details	£	Discrepancies
3 May	Invoice 2471	1,659	No discrepancy
10 May	Credit note 85	-210	Incorrect amount
21 May	Invoice 2523	1,345	Incorrect date
25 May	Credit note 91	-47	Incorrectly recorded
30 May	Invoice 2547	2,106	Incorrect invoice number

(b)

Balance of Blanca Ltd's receivables account	✔
£184 underpaid	
£184 overpaid	✔
£47 underpaid	
£47 overpaid	

(c)   £2,875.08*

   * £2,470 - £74.10 PPD = £2,395.90 + £479.18 VAT = £2,875.08

(d)

Date 20-6	Detail	£	Outstanding amount £
1 May	Opening balance	2,545	1,000
10 May	Invoice 2495	1,629	443
25 May	Credit note 90	−186	0

Task 5

(a)

Daybook	✔
Sales day book	
Purchases returns day book	
Purchases day book	✔
Discounts received day book	

Date 20-4	Name	Invoice number	Total £	VAT £	Net £
2 June	Stanton & Co	3684	879.84	146.64	733.30
10 June	Quinn Trading Ltd	49175	1,315.80	219.30	1,096.50
12 June	Patel Supplies	P1079	746.94	124.49	622.45
20 June	Garcia Goods	GG/685	1,825.08	304.18	1,520.90
28 June	Quinn Trading Ltd	49231	1,263.00	210.50	1,052.50
	TOTALS		6,030.66	1,005.11	5,025.55

(b)

Discrepancy	✔
Buyer details	✔
Quantity of goods	
Date of credit note	
Net amount	✔
VAT amount	✔
Total amount	

Task 6

(a)

Purpose	Document
A document issued by the seller to the buyer reducing the amount owing	Credit note
A document issued by the seller stating the amount owing and the terms of payment	Invoice
A document authorised and issued by the buyer and sent to the seller stating the goods required	Purchase order

(b)

Manners & Co
Thorpe Road, Underwood, UN2 5PA
STATEMENT OF ACCOUNT: Sabir Ltd

Date 20-8	Document number	Details	Amount £	✔
3 April	CN 741	Goods returned	−310	
14 April	3218	Goods	1,618	
20 April	3376	Goods	796	
22 April	3410	Goods	895	✔
26 April	3521	Goods	1,024	
18 April	CN 758	Goods returned	−110	✔
30 April	3652	Goods	1,214	✔

(c)

Customer	£	Date
Davenport Ltd	877.50	23 May 20-1
Kazeem Supplies Ltd	1,411.20	26 May 20-1

Task 7

(a)

Cash book	✔
Cash book – receipts	✔
Cash book – payments	

Description for details column	✔
Total	
VAT	
Trade receivables	
Sales	✔

Date 20-8	Details	Total £	VAT £	Net £
5 Jun	Sales	3,019.62	503.27	2,516.35

(b)

Information required	Document
Details of payments made to credit suppliers	Internet banking payments schedule
Details of recurring payments made through the bank account	Standing order and direct debit schedule

Task 8

(a)

VAT £	Net £
3.17	15.85

(b) £61.06

(c)

Details	Amount £	Debit ✔	Credit ✔
Bank	227.64	✔	

Task 9

Cash book	✔
Cash book – receipts	
Cash book – payments	✔

Date 20-6	Details	Total £	VAT £	Net £	Frequency	Recurrences
1 April	Rent paid	800	0	800	Monthly	12

Details	✔
Rent paid	✔
Rent received	
Cash payments	
Office equipment	

Frequency	✔
Daily	
Weekly	
Monthly	✔
Annually	

Task 10

(a)

Account name	Amount £	Debit ✔	Credit ✔
Sales returns	495	✔	
VAT	99	✔	
Receivables ledger control			✔

(b)

Account name	Amount £	Debit ✔	Credit ✔
Mansi Ltd	66	✔	

Task 11

(a)

Account name	Balance £	Debit ✔	Credit ✔
Office equipment	5,405	✔	

(b)

20-1	Details	Amount £	20-1	Details	Amount £
12 April	Bank	2,712	1 April	Balance b/f	3,409
18 April	Purchases Returns	138	24 April	Purchases	1,284
30 April	Balance c/d	1,843			
	Total	4,693		Total	4,693
			1 May	Balance b/d	1,843

Answers to practice assessment 2

Task 1

(a)

Purpose	Document/Record
To list account balances in order to check that the value of debit entries and credit entries is equal	Trial balance
The first place to record financial documents in the accounting system	Book of prime entry
To record cash payments for small purchases and small payments	Petty cash book
To locate the accounting records of individual suppliers who supply on credit to the business	Receivables ledger control account
To tell the business how much is owing from all its customers	Receivables ledger control account

(b)

Date 20-2	Product	Produce code
12 Feb	Envelopes, white	ENWH84
14 Feb	Folders, green	FOGR85
16 Feb	Pens, red	PERE86

(c)

Statement	True ✔	False ✔
Payables ledger control account is a book of prime entry		✔
The statement of profit or loss gives a 'snapshot' of the assets, liabilities and capital of a business at a particular date		✔

(d)

Statement	True ✔	False ✔
The transfer of data into the control accounts is automatic	✔	
Duplication of transactions is prevented		✔

Task 2

(a)

Account	Classification
Rent received	Income
Vehicles	Asset
Payables	Liability
Bank charges	Expense

(b) £90,616

(c)

Transaction	Dual effect
Purchased office equipment using a bank overdraft	Increase in asset and liability
Owner transfers a vehicle into the business	Increase in asset and capital
Trade payables account settled using a bank overdraft	Increase and decrease of liabilities
Bank loan repaid from cash at bank	Decrease in asset and liability
Trade receivable's account settled in cash	Increase and decrease of assets

Task 3

(a)

	£
Amount before discount	2,400.00
Trade discount	120.00
Amount after discount	2,280.00
VAT at 20%	456.00
Total	2,736.00

(b)

Daybook	✔
Sales day book	✔
Sales returns day book	
Purchases day book	
Purchases returns day book	
Discounts allowed day book	
Discounts received day book	

Date 20-4	Customer code	Customer	Invoice number	Total £	VAT £	Net £	G330 £	G331 £	G332 £
8 June	OK03	Okeze Ltd	4576	2,736.00	456.00	2,280.00		2,280.00	

Task 4

(a)   Sutton plc has underpaid the amount owing.

This means that a request for a further payment should be made.

(b)

Outstanding invoices	Total £	VAT £	Net £	Amount to be paid £
5635	2,814	469	2,345	2,743.65
5682	1,290	215	1,075	1,257.75
5705	1,020	170	850	994.50
			Total	4,995.90

(c)

Transaction	Details	Amount £	Action
Balance b/f		1,608.70	Allocate full amount
Invoice 5502	Delivery note 6271	493.60	Allocate part payment
Invoice 5610	Delivery note 6742	638.40	Allocate full amount
Credit note 491	Overcharge re invoice 5610	120.00	Allocate full amount

Task 5

(a)

Module option	✔
Sales day book	
Sales returns day book	
Purchases day book	✔
Purchases returns day book	
Discounts allowed day book	
Discounts received day book	

Date 20-2	Supplier code	Supplier	General ledger code	Invoice number	Net £	VAT code
10 April	KU02	Kumar Ltd	4174	27451	1,564.00	VAT4

(b)

Discrepancy	✔
Quantity supplied	
Product supplied	✔
Date of invoice	
Unit price	
Net amount	
VAT amount	✔
Total amount	✔
Terms of payment	✔

Task 6

(a)　(i)

Date	✔
20 April	
30 April	
10 May	✔
11 May	
20 May	
31 May	

(ii)

Terms of payment	Amount to be paid £	Date by which supplier should receive payment
Payment within 20 days	6,938.40	30 April
Payment within 10 days	6,867.60	20 April

(b)

Supplier report Southern Suppliers				
Date 20-3	Transaction type	Details	£	✔
1 April	BAL	Balance b/f	4,512	✔
2 April	SCN	Credit note 1217	238	✔
10 April	SI	Invoice 4538	1,726	
12 April	SI	Invoice 4603	2,134	✔
18 April	SI	Invoice 4725	896	
20 April	SI	Invoice 4812	1,522	✔
22 April	SI	Invoice 4867	943	
25 April	SI	Invoice 4938	646	
29 April	BP	Bank payment 074324	4,274	
30 April	BP	Bank payment 074327	3,656	

(c)　£4,211

Task 7

(a)

Module option	✔
Cash book – receipts	✔
Cash book – payments	
Petty cash book – receipts	
Petty cash book – payments	

Date 20-3	Details	General ledger code	Document number	Net £	VAT code
2 May	Wyvern Agency	6050	574	600.00	VAT1
2 May	Nelson & Co	3600	621	346.50	VAT4

(b)   £ | −1,505.52 |

Task 8

(a)

Details	Amount £	Debit ✔	Credit ✔
Balance carried down	70.79*		✔

* £25.47 + £250.00 − £204.68 = £70.79

(b)

Date 20-2	Details	Total £	VAT £	Net £
1 May	Office Supplies Ltd	24.78	4.13	20.65

Task 9

Transaction type: Recurring payment	
Details	460 Office expenses
Payee	Vale Services Limited
Sort code	20-18-34
Account number	10045671
Start date	10 May 20-3
Frequency	Monthly
Recurrences	12
End date	10 April 20-4
Amount	£78.60
VAT code	VAT4

Task 10

(a)

Account name	Amount £	Debit ✔	Credit ✔
Purchases returns	656.00		✔
VAT	131.20		✔
Payables ledger control	787.20	✔	

(b)

Ledger	✔
Payables	
Receivables	✔

(c)

Account name	Amount £	Debit ✔	Credit ✔
Gomez Ltd	56.40		✔

Task 11

(a)

Details	Amount £	Debit ✔	Credit ✔
Balance c/d	1,243		✔

(b) £2,098

(c)

Account code	Details	Amount £	Debit ✔	Credit ✔
RL130	Balance b/d	336	✔	
PL235	Balance b/d	268		✔

Answers to practice assessment 3

Task 1

(a)

Purpose	Document/Record
Detailing credit customer transactions and issued, often at the month-end, to encourage payment of amounts owing	Statement of account
Detailing all general ledger debit and credit balances which are totalled to give a preliminary check of the accuracy of the bookkeeping system	Trial balance
Detailing goods which have been returned by credit customers and which gives a reduction in the amount owing to the seller	Credit note
Detailing the payment of low-value business expenses made in cash for a period, often a month, the balance of which is topped up from the bank	Petty cash book

(b)

Customer name	Customer account code
Grundy Goods	GR003
Stewart Ltd	ST002

(c)

	✔
Purchases day book	✔
Purchases returns day book	
Sales day book	
Sales returns day book	
Cash book	

(d)

Statement	True ✔	False ✔
Receivables ledger control account shows the total amount owing to suppliers		✔
The owner's capital account always has a credit balance	✔	
A trial balance that balances proves that the bookkeeping is accurate		✔

Task 2

(a)

Account	Asset ✔	Liability ✔	Income ✔	Expense ✔
Rent received			✔	
Office equipment	✔			
Payables		✔		
Wages and salaries				✔

(b)   £21,771

(c)

Transaction	Dual effect
Owner pays money into the bank to reduce the bank overdraft	Increase in capital and decrease in a liability
Bank payment made from overdrawn bank account to settle payables' accounts	Increase and decrease in a liability
Purchased office equipment on credit from Wyvern Office Limited	Increase in both an asset and a liability
Old office equipment sold for cash	Increase and decrease in an asset
A receivables account is settled by cheque which is paid into the bank to reduce the overdraft	Decrease in both an asset and a liability

Task 3

(a)

	£
Amount before discount	1,530.00
Bulk discount	76.50
Amount after discount	1,453.50
VAT at 20%	290.70
Total	1,744.20

(b)

Daybook	✔
Sales day book	
Sales returns day book	✔
Purchases day book	
Purchases returns day book	
Discounts allowed day book	
Discounts received day book	

(c)

Date 20-4	Customer code	Customer	Invoice number	Total £	VAT £	Net £	T110 £	T115 £	T120 £
1 June	GO02	Goode Ltd	CN 247	1,744.20	290.70	1,453.50		1,453.50	

Task 4

(a)

20-5	Details	£	Discrepancies
3 June	Invoice 5042	3,068	Incorrect invoice number
10 June	Credit note 92	−165	Incorrectly recorded
21 June	Invoice 5738	2,465	Incorrect date
25 June	Credit note 104	−79	Incorrect amount
30 June	Invoice 6014	1,411	No discrepancy

(b)

Balance of King Ltd's receivables account	✔
(a) £312 underpaid	
(b) £312 overpaid	✔
(c) £79 underpaid	
(d) £79 overpaid	

(c) £1,693.44*

    * £1,728 ÷ 1.2 = £1,440 - £28.80 PPD = £1,411.20 + £282.24 VAT = £1,693.44

(d)

Date 20-5	Detail	£	Outstanding amount £
1 June	Opening balance	1,822	822
10 June	Invoice 5431	1,027	0
25 June	Credit note 105	−95	0

Task 5

(a)

Module option	✔
Sales day book	
Sales returns day book	
Purchases day book	✔
Purchases returns day book	
Discounts allowed day book	
Discounts received day book	

Date 20-8	Supplier code	Supplier	General ledger code	Invoice number	Net £	VAT code
12 Oct	WR001	Wright Ltd	5176	35472	1,537.50	VAT4

(b)

Discrepancy	✔
Quantity supplied	✔
Product supplied	
Date of invoice	
Unit price	✔
Net amount	
VAT amount	
Total amount	✔
Terms of payment	✔

Task 6

(a)

Purpose	Document
A document issued by the seller stating the cost at which goods or services can be provided	Quotation
A document issued by the seller listing the goods and accompanying them	Delivery note
A document issued by the seller listing invoices, credit notes and payments on the account and stating a total amount due	Statement of account

(b)

Marr & Co
Wills Road, Wyvern WV1 3QX
STATEMENT OF ACCOUNT: Sebright Ltd

Date 20-6	Document number	Details	Amount £	✔
3 May	CN 481	Goods returned	−134	
14 May	SI 4785	Goods	1,428	
20 May	SI 4896	Goods	867	
22 May	SI 4945	Goods	1,045	✔
26 May	SI 5211	Goods	2,013	
18 May	CN 502	Goods returned	−85	✔
30 May	SI5652	Goods	1,319	✔

(c)

Customer	£	Date
Castille Ltd	698.40	27 May 20-6
Savin Supplies Ltd	491.40	22 May 20-6

Task 7

(a)

Module option	✔
Cash book – receipts	
Cash book – payments	✔
Petty cash book – receipts	
Petty cash book – payments	

Date 20-7	Details	General ledger code	Document number	Net £	VAT code
11 Aug	Blenheim Lettings	6100	341	800.00	VAT1
11 Aug	Martin's Garage Ltd	7820	342	451.60	VAT4

(b)   £2,039.77

Task 8

(a)

VAT £	Net £
2.10	10.50

(b)   £73.92

(c)

Details	Amount £	Debit ✔	Credit ✔
Bank	164.57	✔	

Task 9

Cash book	✔
Cash book – receipts	
Cash book – payments	✔

Date 20-3	Details	Total £	VAT £	Net £	Frequency	Recurrences
1 Jun	Cleaning	1,380	230	1,150	Monthly	12

Details	
Stationery	
Cleaning	✔
Cash payments	
Office equipment	

Frequency	
Daily	
Weekly	
Monthly	✔
Annually	

Task 10

(a)

Account name	Amount £	Debit ✔	Credit ✔
Sales	6,825		✔
VAT	1,365		✔
Receivables ledger control	8,190	✔	

(b)

Account name	Amount £	Debit ✔	Credit ✔
Nelson Ltd	42		✔

Task 11

(a)

Details	Amount £	Debit ✔	Credit ✔
Balance c/d	1,602	✔	

(b) £2,344

(c)

Account code	Details	Amount £	Debit ✔	Credit ✔
RL640	Balance b/d	384	✔	
PL1050	Balance b/d	567		✔

for your notes

for your notes

for your notes

for your notes

for your notes

for your notes

for your notes

for your notes

for your notes

_____

for your notes

for your notes

for your notes

for your notes

for your notes

for your notes

for your notes

for your notes

for your notes

for your notes

for your notes

for your notes

for your notes

for your notes